ANIMAL IMPRINTS

MURPHYS WRITERS

For information about this book contact
Marlene Wiley Bradford
Murphys, California
209-728-8213

Printed by WORD*PRO* PRESS
410 East Upland Road, Ithaca, New York 14850

This book is dedicated to the
Calaveras County Humane Society,
a local volunteer group that works
to save animals and find them homes.

Introduction

A book of animal stories? Sure! Everyone loves animals.
Our Murphys Writers discussed the good idea and came to
almost immediate agreement. Our resident artist looked
forward to making animal drawings. Several others got
dreamy looks as they remembered beloved pets that had
enriched their youth—or age.

Several weeks later little bubbles of uneasiness floated to
the surface at our group meeting. Some of us didn't have
wonderful pet memories. In fact, some of us weren't comfortable
around most animals—wild or domestic. But as we worked
through this new information, we discovered we each had
some strong feelings about the creatures around us, negative
and positive. And we had some questions as well about how
animal lore seems to pervade our culture.

In a circular movement, we came back to our original thought:
A book of animal stories? Sure!

Thus *Animal Imprints* began. We hope you enjoy our free
soaring through the loves and dislikes of people and their pets,
their encounters with the wild.

Contents

From My Window

Touched by a Dog

Near the Barnyard

Stuffed with Love

Imprints

Preface

Murphys Writers presents our fifth publication. The first four, *The Amber Necklace, Seeds, Seeds 2,* and *Paper Snowflakes,* have become bookshelf friends of local and distant readers.

Animals with which we share our world are a source of wonder to most of us. We watch them, love or fear them, and enlist some of them as helpers in our lives. Each of us has experiences with and feelings about furry, feathered, or scaly creatures. *Animal Imprints* relates stories of our own encounters and relationships with members of the animal kingdom.

Thank you to each of the Murphys Writers, who contributed to this group project writing and discussing our stories, helping with distribution and publicity, and planning our celebration party. We give special thanks to our editors and proofreaders, Grace Muirhead, Faye Morrison, and Barbara Conrad, to Lois Grisdale, who conceived the idea of this book, created the drawings, and designed its pages and cover, and who also created the art work for our previous three books. And to Marlene Wiley Bradford who prepared the book for printing.

Part of the proceeds from sales of *Animal Imprints* will be donated to the Calaveras County Humane Society.

December, 2005
Murphys, California

Cat Tales

Purr

Arlene Mueller

While I nap
my cat
curls
around my neck
like a collar
my chin resting
in the soft fur
absorbing her deep purr.
It's enough.

The Cat from Klatt

Yolanda Randlett

Max gazed lazily out the window, warming his back in the Alaska summer sun. He spent a fair amount of time on his carpeted ledge in the living room, watching the seasons change from comforting warmth to frightening cold. He liked the summer best.

His preferred spot in Julie's townhouse was her bed because there her scent was strongest; he relished her odor, feeling she was always near. His favorite game was to stare at her with his golden eyes, pounce when she was asleep, and nibble her nose. Sometimes he purred so loud and long his saliva dribbled on her face. When she became irritated and ordered him to go away, he didn't mind. She kept a water dish for him by her closet. After rippling the water with his paw, he would take a drink, lie down, and wait until she was ready to pet him again. He purred when she brushed his long gray fur, removing any hint of tangles. He loved being clean.

Max met Julie at the Humane Society one March weekend several years ago. He had been barely surviving by making a nuisance of himself at restaurants on Klatt Street in Anchorage when somebody turned him in. It was just as well. Living alone was tough. His skinny body lay hidden under matted, dirty fur. He had been declawed. Without the extra holding power that claws provide, he had a hard time climbing any higher than he could jump. He limped as a result of falling from dumpsters trying to get food. Thirst was an even greater problem because water froze in winter. His tongue stuck to the ice, ripping when he tried to get it free, until he learned to test the water with his paw to make sure it was liquid instead of solid.

Julie didn't know his story when she brought him to her home, but his long handsome coat, golden eyes, sweet disposition, and paws without claws suggested he had been a pampered cat until he was abandoned. Why did Max's first home disappear? Was he lost or left during a move, maybe by a military family? Perhaps packing had made him nervous and he hid so well that when it was time to catch an airplane, nobody could find him. In any case, he had been resourceful enough to survive homeless for several months of winter in Anchorage.

Now he was content and hardly remembered a time without Julie. However, when the days grew shorter and colder with the coming of winter, Max became anxious. He pawed the bed, trying to hide in the blankets. He rippled the water more than usual before taking a drink. He hated the cold and refused to go outside, especially if it was snowing.

Now the summer's growing sun warmed Max's belly as it shined through the window on his outstretched body. The front door opened and Julie's cheery voice called out, "Max, I'm home." Jumping to the floor, he ran to greet her as he meowed the news of the day. Each time he rippled the water it was liquid, her scent on the bed told him he was not alone, and his nap had been refreshing. All in all, life was good. 🐾

Life Lesson Taught by a Cat

Marian Cramer

No one recalls exactly when or how Panther joined our family. Either he was a stray cat that followed one of us home or he showed up on the doorstep. Naturally we fed him and like the Broadway play, he became "the man who came to dinner." And stayed.

He was totally black with a healthy sleek coat—naming him Panther was more obvious than creative. The part we got wrong was that within days we noted a swollen belly and knew it was time to change his name to Pantheretta. Even when we knew better, we still called her Panther.

Our family pet shared her care and also lap time except with our father. He tolerated her with kindness, but I never saw Panther purring on his lap. In time Panther decided where to make her birthing center, but her naïve new owners were clueless about this process. One day someone opened the downstairs coat closet and screamed, "Panther had her babies!" She had not asked for help and she didn't get any. Who knew? My mother silently threw away the jacket Panther had managed to pull from a hook and make into her maternity bed. She was a better feline than we were pet parents. While we hovered, Panther took care of her babies.

The kittens were given away, and a local vet arranged for Panther to have no further need of the coat closet birthing center. Life went on. Panther was considered the family pet, but we always knew that she owned us because her haughty independence clearly announced her role as alpha cat.

Panther matured along with her adopted human family. Lee and I became teenagers whose social lives were active and not cat-centered. Panther was a frequent observer of our teenaged angst. She watched with sleepy eyes while our mother pleaded with us to give her a break. "Girls, I wish you would come home early tonight. I am exhausted and want to get some sleep." Mother was a kindergarten teacher and every Friday she was beyond tired.

"But Motherrrrrr," we whined, "just go to bed and sleep. We'll be fine. And if we aren't, we'll call you. Honest!" Lee and I rolled our eyes and left the room, impatiently discussing our mother's stubborn refusal to just go to sleep when we were out.

One night after the dishes were done, I opened the kitchen door and called for Panther, who usually sailed through the doorway and skidded across the kitchen floor in her haste to find a good lap for the evening. But on this night, no flash of satin black approached. I marched to the front door and repeated my plea. Lee joined my concern and as the older sister, she went out into the dark yard while I remained on the porch softly calling, "Here kitty, kitty." Panther had never answered a kitty call, but it was all I could think of to do. Eventually we closed the doors and began to attack homework assignments. I sat at the kitchen counter on a high stool, but Lee had gone upstairs to her room.

I only half concentrated on what I was reading because most of my brain was occupied with desperate listening for a cat's meow. The slightest sound got me up to open the door and call again, "Panther, come in. Here kitty, kitty." The cold made it hard to stand very long in the open doorway. I stayed until my fingers were numb, but no cat appeared.

The important history test the next morning demanded that I study. I turned back to the books, but it was no use. I jumped back and forth between worry and anger. If Panther had walked into the room, she would have been in mortal danger from her stressed-out owner. Concentration was impossible.

That night I heard tires squealing and brakes screeching far too often on our busy street. My heart pounded as I awaited the sound of impact. Father came into the kitchen and told me it was late and I should get to bed. "But Daddy," I pleaded, "I have to wait up for Panther."

"Panther will be at the back door in the morning," he responded. "You have school tomorrow. Let's go." I knew my father, and this was a command, not a suggestion. I looked outside again, but only darkness looked back. I went upstairs.

I put on my pajamas and brushed my teeth, but before I crawled into bed I needed to call Panther one more time. My bare feet made no sound as I sneaked down the back stairs. I tiptoed to the front window. I watched car headlights come and go in each direction. In the glow of their lights I searched the neighbors' darkened yards, seeking some sign of Panther. As I rested my head on the windowsill, I was surprised to discover I had trouble keeping my eyes open. My hope for a good mark on the history test faded. My feet were cold. But the idea of returning to my warm bed upstairs was unthinkable.

Suddenly two bright eyes glinted at the end of the Dixons' driveway across the street. *Panther! She's home!* She darted into the street just as a car came speeding toward town. I wailed like a banshee and tried to run out the locked door to rescue my beloved cat, but my father's hand closed over mine. He unlocked the door and stepped out on the porch. "Here she is," he said as our cool cat strode into the house and headed straight for the kitchen and the food she knew would be in her bowl.

"I'm sorry, Dad. I know I should be in bed but I couldn't sleep until Panther came home. I was just too worried."

"I understand how it is," he sighed. "I can't sleep because your mother can't sleep when you girls are out on dates." As a contented Panther strolled to her basket and settled down for the night, I sighed with relief and headed upstairs. I, too, finally understood what loving worry was. 🐾

Two Litters to a Lug

Marlene Wiley Bradford

Part I

We brought Misty home when she was a tiny fluffy white kitten. Only part Persian, she inherited the personality of her tabby forbears—common, friendly, and rambunctious. She learned early to climb trees, chase little balls, and play with catnip mice. All three of our young children held her, pulled her in their wagons, and took naps with her.

She grew into a lovely cat. When she was nearly a year old, I noticed her growing tummy and realized she soon would present us with kittens.

I felt her time must be getting near when I found Misty resting comfortably on top of a cardboard box inside a garage cabinet. Assuming she decided to use that place, I mentally agreed it would be perfect for her. She had entered when the cabinet door was closed by walking between the studs behind the cabinet. Of course, other cats would be able to do so as well, but no other cats had ever come into our garage—so far.

I placed an empty wooden lug box lined with clean soft rags where Misty had been sleeping, then put her into it. She curled up, purred, and continued with her nap.

The next morning I found a smaller, black short-haired cat sitting with Misty next to her dish. Although I intended to put the black cat outside, after looking into her round yellow eyes, I fed breakfast to both cats. The black cat stayed close to Misty, who accepted her as though they'd been friends for ages. The demure black kitty was thin but her large belly looked suspiciously pregnant.

That evening my husband said, "We'd better not keep that other cat."

"Well, what do you want me to do?" I asked. He said he didn't know, and I didn't, either.

The black cat stayed in our garage with Misty, without invading the lug box, and the next morning we found Misty inside her box with six colorful short-haired babies.

As our three young children and I sat gently petting the little newborns, listening to their soft mewling and watching them try to walk on wobbly legs, the black cat climbed into the box. I picked her up and put her out. She climbed back in and began licking the kittens. *Well,* I thought, *Misty doesn't seem to mind.* I decided to let the two cats work it out.

The next morning, the black cat was in the lug box giving birth to her second kitten. Misty jumped into it, began licking one of her kittens, and settled down to nurse them while Blackie was washing her new kitten. Then Blackie lay down to nurse while Misty jumped out of the box. Blackie nursed and licked whichever of the kittens was nearby. Soon, Misty got into the box, and the two mother cats lay encircling all the babies with their warm tummies and furry legs. The eight kittens lined up, some facing the white mom and the others facing the black one. Now and then one babe would let go of her teat, nuzzle another kitten, give a high squeaky meow, and turn around to nurse on the other mother.

There was a lot of purring, licking, kneading of little paws. Neither Misty nor Blackie cared which babes belonged to her, and both benefited from the joint venture. Usually one of the mothers was in the box when the other left for a while, except when I fed them dinner. Both cats were always hungry and ate together, each from her own dish.

We left the group for a weekend to visit grandparents. As we drove along the highway, we saw a large truck fully loaded with lug boxes on its way to a cannery. Our four-year-old daughter, Robyn, looked at the truck and asked, "Mommy, are all those boxes full of baby kitties?"

I kept myself from laughing, but with a grin explained that lug boxes were made to carry fruit and vegetables to packing houses and canneries. The cat's lug box had been full of pears. Our family then adopted the private joke of pointing to produce trucks along the highway with the remark, "Look, there's a truckload of kittens."

After we found homes for the kittens, Blackie disappeared, and we never saw her again. We had no idea where she had come from or where she went.

Part II

When we realized Misty was expecting again and her lug box was ready, she had three furry babies, two white and one striped. Soon after their birth the large garage car door was open, and a boxer dog wandered in. I was totally taken by surprise to see our dear docile cat turn into a flying-tiger monster. She yowled and hissed as she chased that dog at least two houses from us and walked triumphantly back to her kittens. The dog never returned.

However, a few days later we saw a large, orange long-haired tomcat in our back yard. *Don't tomcats sometimes hurt kittens?* I thought. *Those were only stories, weren't they?* Besides, Misty had shown she could protect her babes.

We didn't see the tomcat again for two weeks. The kittens were bright-eyed and bouncing around their box, even trying to stand on two legs to reach the top. From the kitchen we heard sounds of a terrible cat fight in our garage. Quickly I pulled open the door to see the red tomcat rushing out the back door of the garage with Misty in pursuit. Hearing kittens loudly crying, we threw open the cabinet door and to our horror, we saw one of the babies lying still, with puncture wounds.

We buried the little dead kitten under our Peace rose bush and placed a small stone over his head. Furthermore, we kept the garage doors closed. But that wasn't enough for Misty. The next evening while I cooked dinner, I heard a crying kitten inside the wall between our kitchen and the garage.

When I went to investigate, Misty was carrying a kitten in her mouth, jumping from our dryer up to the top of a high cabinet. I tried to call her back as she carried the kitten between the blades of the fan (which was not turned on) and into our attic. The lug box was empty. I figured she had already carried the other kitten up to the attic and, left alone, he had walked to the edge of the crawl-space and fallen between the Sheetrock, landing on the 2 by 4 brace halfway between the floor and ceiling.

The kitten continued to cry between the walls while I shed tears into my simmering stew. Misty was also crying, as was the other little kitten. The children worried and voiced my concerns: "How can we get the kitten out? What are we going to do?"

When my husband arrived home, he asked what in the world was going on. Wasting no time, he got a screwdriver and the long ladder, removed the fan, and reached down to retrieve the stranded kitten. His arm was not long enough for that, but he managed to lift Misty and the other kitten down. We took them safely into the house until we could figure out what to do about our stranded babe. "I guess we'll have to break a hole in the wall," he said.

"Oh, wait. I have an idea," I said. "Here's a diaper. Try dangling it down in the space next to the kitten. Shake it up and down." Just as I had hoped, the kitten grabbed the long piece of cloth with his sharp little claws, and my husband pulled him up. Soon thereafter, he replaced the fan and installed chicken wire around it.

Misty and her family settled back down in the cabinet again for a few more weeks until we found homes for her last two kittens. We retired her from kitten production and let her enjoy being a pampered household cat, napping near sunny windows. 🐾

Miss Kitty

Jan Overstreet

Our cat is no longer with us, and what an enormous relief that is. She has gone to be with the rest of the cats that live just behind The Tree House boutique; she will have lots of company and I'm sure she will be delighted. Linda, the dear woman who owns The Tree House, takes in any and all stray cats, and even an occasional dog.

It's not as though Miss Kitty were ugly or whiny. Actually, when she wasn't destroying everything she touched, she was rather sweet. She would eat absolutely anything at any time without ever making a mess, which is certainly more than can be said for our human progeny!

She did, however, have some less-than-charming habits. For instance, the skirt of our newly reupholstered chair was too tempting for her to resist. It now resembles a badly stained curtain that looks as though it has been there since Adam.

What finally led to the parting of the ways between me and Miss Kitty was the blood. Not on her, of course, just on me, from elbow to wrist (and on the carpeted floor—beige, naturally). Miss Kitty had sprung uninvited onto my lap, where she promptly began nibbling on my arm. I was not thrilled by this touching moment, but at least she hadn't drawn blood yet. Cleverly she had deduced that nibbling was OK. I gently shoved her off my lap, hoping there would be no consequences. Bad management on my part, but there you go. Silly me. Back she came, and this time she was literally out for blood. I should have known better than to push her off my lap again, but I didn't. As for me, a quick downward glance revealed the blood dripping from my arm onto the carpet, more blood than I am accustomed to dealing with, nor do I plan to deal with it—ever again. Meanwhile Miss Kitty dashed across the room to attack the chair skirt once again.

I suppose if I were more warm-hearted, Miss Kitty would still be living with us, but I am not and she is not, and I think we will both live happily ever after. 🐾

Didit

Grace Muirhead

We had a tiny kitten. Didit was her name. We also had a baby named Jenifer and another baby on the way.

With fumbling, pudgy little hands, Jenifer had plucked Didit from a litter of motherless kittens to be her first pet. When we asked her what the kitty's name was going to be, she grinned and lisped in two-year-old fashion, "Didit." So Didit it was.

Didit actually turned out to be my second child. She was much too young to be without a mother, who had been killed when a car hit her. Having lots of baby paraphernalia around, I used some of it to take care of Didit. From a medicine dropper I fed her milk mixed with baby rice cereal as I cupped her in my hand. Many times I found myself with both Jenifer and Didit in my lap while Jenifer and I took turns doing the feeding. It was a tender time shared with two soft, cuddly, and trusting small beings. Sometimes Jenifer and I serenaded Didit with a sentimental nursery song:

> I love little pussy, her coat is so warm
> And if I don't hurt her she'll do me no harm
> I'll sit by the fire and feed her some food
> And pussy will love me because I am good.

Jenifer and Didit enjoyed livelier times together as well. Jenifer laughed in delight as Didit chased a ball of crumpled paper around the kitchen. And Jenifer's blond ringlets bounced around her rosy-cheeked toddler face as she enticed Didit to chase the string that she dangled for Didit to swat.

When Jenifer was napping or in bed for the evening, Didit would cuddle up in the cushion of my palm and suck the skin between my thumb and forefinger. Her scratchy tongue was comforting.

She eventually grew too large to fit in my hand, but she remained affectionate and cuddly, often curling herself over my shoulder. Besides that, she had a full-time purring motor. How I loved that kitten!

And almost everyone else did, too. The single exception that I knew of was Kalpakam Desai, the wife of a graduate student in my husband's department. Although I didn't know her very well, I agreed to host a baby shower for her. Didit was her liveliest that evening, perhaps excited by the flurry of visitors with their clattering high-heeled shoes and high-pitched chatter. Being from India, Kalpakam had dressed herself elegantly in a silken, richly colored sari. And being from India, she was unfamiliar with local customs and somewhat apprehensive about the party in her honor.

Early in the party Didit alternated between kittenish careening around the room and pouncing and attacking. Her first target of note was the sari. Horrified gasps and squawks ensued as Didit scuttled up the silk. Kalpakam recoiled, unable to hide her distress under her polite demeanor. Didit was banished to the back yard for the rest of the evening. The claw marks in the silk disappeared, too, after I nervously manipulated the pulls in the fabric with my fingertips.

As time went on, I made a trek to Tompkins County Hospital to deliver my second natural child, another daughter. Upon arriving home with new daughter in my arms, I noticed that

Didit didn't come running out to greet me. My husband, Joe, confessed that he'd put Didit outside so she wouldn't tear up the house when no one was there, and that Didit had been missing for a couple of days. He had called for her every night, but she hadn't responded with her usual energetic bounce through the door.

I took in this information standing on the doorstep, beautiful baby Anne sleeping peacefully in my arms in contrast to the agitation I felt. There was nothing—not a thing!—in that cheaply furnished grad student apartment that Didit could harm. No fine fabric. The furniture was about as battered as furniture could be. How could he have turned her out?

In the midst of my trauma, still standing outside the door, I noticed something welcome: two yellow eyes peering at me from under the sandbox. *Could it be Didit?* I softly called her name. Oh joy—it *was* Didit. There she was. But . . . but something was wrong. Her sweet, kittenish face was drawn, feral. As she approached, running crookedly, I handed baby Anne to her father and stooped down to draw Didit into my arms.

I gasped. She was bent, broken. Numb, I turned her over to Joe and carried Anne into the apartment. Anne and I sat on the couch much the same way Didit and I had positioned ourselves when we relaxed together. Happiness and sadness collided silently in my brain. In the still moments, I found myself unable to think about anything at all.

Pretty soon, the silence ended when Joe came into the room. He had placed Didit in a box in the car and would take her to a vet to see what could be done for her. While he was gone, I nursed Anne and half-heartedly welcomed my landlady, who wanted a peek at the new being. I was still trying to be hospitable when Joe arrived home, having picked up Jenifer from a friend's house where she had been staying.

This, I knew, was a most important moment in Jenifer's life, meeting her sister for the first time. Jenifer was more serious than usual, her body and curls without their usual buoyancy. All the preparation for accepting the new member of our family seemed to have subdued her normal effervescence. And my delight at hugging my appealing two-year old cherub was heartfelt as I went through the motions of introducing the two little girls, but Didit's fate was at the forefront of my thoughts. With Jenifer in the room, though, I couldn't very well ask what had happened to my dear pet and hers.

I don't know how long it took to find out the worst. Didit, the vet said, had been hit by a car or kicked by a horse and didn't stand a chance of recovering. He had euthanized her on the spot.

Forgiving Joe was not easy. In fact, I don't know that I ever did. And I'll never know if Jenifer associated her new sister with the loss of her precious kitty. 🐾

Love Invested

Arlene Mueller

As my gray cat
curls on my lap
I draw a short line
with my finger
on her backbone
the make-believe slot
of a piggy bank
where I-can-slip-in-love
to keep her full
when I must go away.

Kitty in a Huff

Nancy Shacklett

One Sunday after church some years ago my husband and I entered the front door of our home. Our daughter Jennifer rushed excitedly to meet us. "You can't guess what just happened," she said. "Bucky went to the toilet in the guest bathroom!"

"What?" we gasped in astonishment.

"Yes. I was sitting on the couch and I heard this splashing sound of water coming from the bathroom. When I went in to see what was going on, there he was, haughtily enthroned, attending to his chores."

We were amused and amazed and we viewed this family cat in a new light. Maybe Bucky was a genius although none of us had ever noticed that side of his character. We began to keep a close eye on him, to see this phenomenon for ourselves. Sure enough, a few days later, when the family was gathered in the living room, we heard the sound of tinkling water from the bathroom. Jennifer urged us to be quiet as we all peeked around the half-open bathroom door. There was Bucky perched on the toilet with his tail artfully curled up. But when he saw the crowd observing him, he gave us a withering look as if to say, "Can't I have a little privacy, for heaven's sake?" He finished his business, jumped down, and went outside to contemplate such rudeness.

And he must have been highly offended because he walked around for some time with a wary and suspicious eye. We never saw him perform again. ❧

Night Visitor

Arlene Mueller

Sometimes in the middle
of the night my cat
uncurls from sleep
pads to my pillow
peers at me
purring deeply.
I lift the blanket,
she slithers in
under my arm.
During that clockless time
I dream of unborn children
she, perhaps, remembers
an earlier dark cat place.
In the morning she's
recurled atop the coverlet.
When I stir,
she opens one eye
denying everything.

The Wild and the Exotic

The Fox in My Woods

Gwen Serrière

Why do you come here—
handsome and furtive—a blur
of orange-gray fur?

Spied you yesterday
in your swift, crafty glory.
You looked back at me.

Do you still have designs
on my silly, fat chickens—
one for your dinner?

Who've you left at home—
a den of small, hungry kits?
Or are you alone?

I'll give you gophers
but you mustn't ask for hens,
you with the yellow eyes.

The Audacious Intruder

Marjorie Griffith

What in the world has happened? My husband, Charlie, and I entered the front door of our home and stared.

Crumpled candy wrappers were scattered all over the entryway as well as the kitchen floor. A mauled empty box that had contained fat-free yogurt rested in the middle of the living room carpet with evidence of the sticky food smeared well into the nap. As I advanced into the kitchen, I noticed the screen door to the back deck was conspicuous by its absence. Checking closely, I saw the screen was there, all right, but it was flat on the deck with a humungous hole through the top. The animal barrier on the lower half was still intact, however.

Our daughter, Sue, brought explanations on her arrival. She had been over in our absence and left for a while without closing the sliding glass door. While she was gone, a black bear had come in and made herself at home, finding candy in the cupboard and nonfat yogurt in the freezer. We noted that she had rejected the Dreyer's chocolate ice cream. Apparently the bear left as Sue arrived back.

After replacing the screen door with one from a downstairs bedroom, we went to bed. After midnight we heard a scratching sound at the back kitchen door—sure enough, our afternoon guest had come back for seconds. Charlie scared her away, but not before she had ruined another screen door.

At this second episode I began to worry. Charlie was leaving for a weekend on his boat and I was to be alone. How was I to cope with a hungry bear? I had Charlie teach me how to use the .22 pistol so that I could scare her away when and if she came to call. Since we live on an isolated eight acres, I had no worries about being a threat to close neighbors.

Two days later our bear arrived again. I heard her out on the deck and peered out to see her standing on her hind feet looking at me through the back door. She was about my height, but I was armed, so I pushed open the sliding glass door shouting at her. She sauntered off the deck, pausing to look back at me. I had the gun in hand and when she stopped, I opened the screen door just enough to fire. Of course, I aimed well over her for I had no intention of doing her harm. I just wanted to scare her. She looked at me, ambled under the tree, squatted to pee and then took herself off at a leisurely walk. My little popgun hadn't even fazed her.

How dare she ignore my efforts to protect my home and food? Furious, I called my son and explained, "I need a gun that makes a *lot* of noise. Could you bring one over and show me how to use it?"

"Yes, Mom, I can," he said, and he did.

Mission accomplished. I now had a shotgun that I could load and fire. I also retrieved from the cupboard a boat horn which made a sound loud enough to carry a mile over water. *Just let that female challenge me, and she'll be sorry. I may be only 5 feet 4 inches, 70 years old, and white haired, but no smart-aleck shaggy-furred mammal is going to flaunt herself at me again.*

A few days passed before I saw my hairy friend again. She shuffled along the driveway toward the house and *my kitchen!* Boy, oh boy! Was she in for a reception!

As she strolled onward, I quietly rolled back the glass door. Horn in hand I waited, and when she turned the corner not three feet from the door, I shoved the screen wide open, jumped out on the deck and—holding the horn directly in front of her nose—pressed the button. Wow! What a noise!

She jumped back, turned, and ran back to the driveway with me in full pursuit, finger hard on the horn button. As she outdistanced me, she turned and paused as if considering where to go next. I wasn't about to let her make her own decision. Running back into the house, I grabbed my trusty loaded shotgun which only needed the safety released. Out on the front porch I could see my adversary still wavering. I braced the rifle on my hip, Annie Oakley style. Once again aiming well above the animal's head, I fired. Oh boy! What a beautiful sound. No indecision now—my woolly friend took off at high speed and crashed through the underbrush all the way to the bottom of the hill.

No. She's not been back.

Clamentine

Carolyn Greenwood

One cat died of oldness
the others got ran over by cars
I am sad sad sad sad
Do you have a pet?
Do you have a pet that diad?
if you do you would know how sad I am
Boo hoo boo hoo
don't you miss your pet that diad?
I miss my pets that diad
did you crie when your pet diad?
wher you sad?
arent you sad sad sad?
I'm sad too
so so so sader than you
well I dont know esaktlee how sad you are
but I'm prety shur I am sadder than you
                    Malia Rose

She was not quite seven, tanned face and pretty hair the color of maple syrup tinged with gold. Natural curls encouraged by the moist sea air bounced unkempt every which way around her face. Malia Rose, a happy child, lived an ordinary life in a small beach community just north of San Francisco.

The one blight in her short life was that she had lost four pet cats to the cars that sped past her house. Stinger, whose tail looked like a bee stinger, met his demise first. Then came Cabo and Lucas, sisters from south of the border. Unfortunately, both loved to hunt mice in the field across the hazardous street. A black long-haired stray, Dancer developed arthritis and no longer could move his feet fast enough to avoid the merciless big black wheels. Betty, the dog of the house, was the only animal to live into her old age and die of just that. She showed no interest in what was on the other side of the fence or across the road, content to stay in the back yard and chase a few birds.

After Betty died, Malia Rose could hardly contain her grief. She had turned eight by then and expressed her sorrow by writing a small book with hand cut pages tied together with a blue ribbon. She dedicated it to Betty and illustrated it with pictures of Betty and herself.

Soon Malia's sorrow ebbed. She began pestering her mom for another dog. She would bury her head in her mother's skirt and weep until she ran out of tears.

"Mommy, I miss Betty so. She was my best friend. Can't we please get a new dog?" the little girl relentlessly implored.

Each time her mother said no. When Malia asked why, she gave Malia the same reasons that a lot of moms give: "We can't afford it. I'll end up feeding it. We'll have to get a sitter for it when we go away."

As gentle as her mother was, the words fell cold and hard upon Malia's ears. No matter how many tears flooded her face, how hard she stamped her foot and wailed, her mother still said no. Malia walked around her house for weeks with droopy shoulders, a constant frown, and an upside-down smile.

Then Malia decided to change her strategy. Hoping to accommodate her mother's need for little cost, little cleanup, and little trouble, she first asked for a snake, then a hamster, then a turtle, and finally a goldfish. Her mother said no to everything.

As sometimes happens when we stop looking so desperately hard for our wants, what we want just drops into our lap. This happened to Malia.

One warm Stinson Beach afternoon, an excited Malia burst through the back door leading with her head, hands behind her back, panting and screaming with delight, "Mommy, Mommy come here! Come see! I have the perfect pet!"

Her mother scrunched her face up like a bulldog. She stood in the middle of the living room rug, hands on hips, lips pinched tight, scowling at the sand falling from Malia's wet feet.

In desperation the little girl cried, "Please Mommy, don't say anything, please! Let me explain. You don't have to pay for any food. It doesn't take up much room. No cleanup. You don't have to get a sitter when we go away! Mommy, it's perfect, absolutely perfect! And besides, I've already named her!"

With her mother stunned into silence, Malia brought her hands from behind her back and with a look of total satisfaction showed her mother a clam that she had named Clamentine. Both mother and daughter stood frozen for a moment, their eyes uneasily searching each other's for a clue to what was next. It was the mother's turn to speak.

She beckoned her daughter to come closer and gazed upon her young pleading face, eyes welling with tears, lips quivering with uncertainty.

"Malia, my darling, I know how anxious you are to have a pet. And yes, you are right. Clamentine won't take up much room and shouldn't be much trouble. And yes, I'll agree to your keeping Clamentine. But I must warn you. Your clam may not live very long because he, excuse me—*she*—is out of her natural environment"

Holding back her tears of relief, Malia flung her arms around her mother's waist. They pulled each other close in a tight hug. Malia softly chanted a litany of, "Thank you, thank you," while her mother whispered back, "It's okay, dear, it's okay."

The little girl heeded her mother's warning. Every day, Malia went down to the ocean to bring back a pail of fresh ocean water and seaweed. She put Clamentine in an old Tupperware box and painted colorful fish on the outside. Some old china dime-store mermaids and pretty rocks decorated the inside. One day she painted a big letter "C" and a blue and white flower on Clamentine's shell. Clamentine would open her shell to search for food, but when Malia tried to pet her, she would close up and remain quiet as a stone most of the day.

A week went by before Malia came to her mother and said, "Mommy I don't think that Clamentine is very happy. Even though I love her, I don't think that we can be best friends because she's afraid of me." Her mother agreed.

The very next day, Malia took Clamentine down to the water's edge. She paused to look out to the immense sea that would claim her clam as its own. A curious dog came by and sniffed at the clam and then went on his way. Malia gently placed Clamentine into the wet sand and as a wave covered her, tearfully said good bye.

This was a big lesson about life and death for a little girl who was only eight years old and had lost four cats, a dog named Betty, and Clamentine. 🐾

Speedy?

Jane Lang

I walked into the kitchen as my son yelled, "Mom, we're home. Where are you? You gotta see what I bought." No movement, no barking, no mewing came from the box our eight-year-old son, Tommy, placed on the kitchen table. His dad had taken him to the pet store, and judging from the wicked gleam in Tommy's eye, I knew I was in for a surprise. Tommy loved attention. The last pet he owned was a chameleon that slept on his shoulder. What strange animal attracted him this time?

Continuing in a very serious tone of voice, Tommy explained, "I found the perfect pet, Mom. I used the gift certificate Billy gave me for my birthday. I'll bet you five dollars no one else has a pet like this." His voice reflected more enthusiasm as he continued, "Dad and I decided we could find a wooden box big enough to give Speedy plenty of room to move around and put glass in the front and back, like what they put plants in. Dad said we can make a top with hinges so I can reach in and take him out. An electric light bulb inside will keep him warm. He can sleep in his house on the headboard of my bed." Tommy pointed to a paper sack. "He eats mealy worms. They're alive and have to be kept in the fridge. OK, Mom?"

Tommy's eyes returned to the container. "Ready, Mom?" He carefully opened the box, with no attempt to lift the occupant out, and stepped aside for me to look.

With a bit of apprehension I peered inside to be greeted by one of two hooded eyes belonging to a grass-green scaly creature about one-and-a-half feet long with a comb-like spinal crest. Long claws extended from his feet, his body ending in a whiplash tail.

Stay calm, I cautioned myself. *Don't overreact.* I concluded this was some kind of a lizard, but not like any I had ever seen. He was completely motionless, except for one eye following my movements. I meekly asked, "What is it, Tommy?"

He proudly announced, "It's a South American iguana, Mom. I found out all about him. He has to be kept warm or he'll die. He's what you call an ex-ex-ex-otic animal or something like that. He has colored scales mixed with the green ones. He moves fast if he wants to, that's why I call him Speedy, but most of the time he just stays still and looks dead. He only changes colors when the light shines on his scales."

This conversation was a bit long for Tommy, but he continued, "He won't be any trouble. He'll live in the box. He has a leash. He can't run away. He can play in the bathtub. Don't worry, Mom. He's not dangerous."

This is a pet? How do you play with an iguana? News traveled fast and all the neighborhood kids came to see this unusual animal. Some handled him with care and others refused to pick him up.

"He's really something, Tommy. Why'd you want him for a pet?" Phil, his best friend, asked.

Tommy grinned. "I think he's neat. I want to show him off. He's easy to take care of and he's different. No one else has a pet like this."

Speedy stayed in the box until his house was finished. Tommy eagerly helped his dad with the construction, using a tape measure, hammer, and other carpenter's tools. He seemed more enthusiastic about building the terrarium than paying attention to his new pet. I could count on my fingers the number of times Tommy handled Speedy. He seemed afraid to hold him for any length of time. I picked Speedy up once and experienced the same reluctance. I touched his sharp scales and claws, and his cold body, and watched those lifeless hooded eyes. He was not a pet to be cuddled.

Occasionally Tommy put the iguana in the bathtub filled with about an inch of water, the only time Speedy became active. He moved frantically all over the slippery surface of the tub. He tried to crawl out, but his claws just slipped on the porcelain. This erratic behavior frightened Tommy, who became more and more content to watch Speedy through the glass in his box, fascinated by the way his long tongue extended to snatch up the mealy worms.

Every time I cleaned my son's room I looked at the lethargic Speedy stretched out in his terrarium, soaking in the heat rays. When the light landed on his scaly back, iridescent colors of red and yellow blended with the green, I had to admit I understood why Tommy was attracted to this tropical creature. I never saw Speedy open his mouth, hiss, or make any noise. *Imagine sleeping with this animal above your head.*

Tommy tolerated Speedy for about six months and then decided he really didn't want to keep this "ex-ex-something" iguana. He had paid him little attention and never attempted to teach him tricks. *What to do with Speedy?*

I remembered my friend Mary, a kindergarten teacher who loved snakes and turtles. She kept them in her classroom to acquaint the children with live animals. Tommy called and asked if she would take Speedy. She answered without hesitation, "Sure, bring him over. I love iguanas."

Tommy arrived with Speedy to share with the excited children. He carefully lifted him up to show how the sun reflected on his scales, spending several minutes telling them all about his South American pet. Speedy remained motionless, except for rotating his hooded eyes to view the world.

Tommy sighed with relief and patted his head before placing him back in his house. With no tears, but a broad smile on his face, Tommy quietly said, "Goodbye, Speedy. Have fun in kindergarten."

As we left the room, he looked at me with a gleam in his eye and said, "Mom, can we stop at the pet store on our way home?"

Bear Burglar

Marjorie Griffith

The day was warm, the action quiet
When first he dared to think of diet.
The way was clear, the door no test
To one of purpose upon a quest.
A simple plunge right through the screen
Put him in front of his fondest dream.
A cupboard! A cupboard—and hardly bare;
Pistachios, chocolates—what fabulous fare!
"Yuck! Why must these folks wrap up each piece
With foil and plastic? Could spoil my feast."
Chew, spit, chew, spit—not good for my health.
I'll just carry it 'round and spread the wealth.
What's this? What's this? This white box so bold?
Methinks I should open it, see what it holds.
Well, well. Would you look 'round in here!
My lucky day is today, one I'll revere.
Butterscotch morsels, and oooh, what a lot!
And these lemon square cookies just hit the spot.
Shall I have little pizzas or bread buttered slick?
That box of See's candy might just do the trick.
Wait a minute! Not so fast! Ice cream also here.
And yogurt. Oh yum. Nonfat. It's quite clear
This place knows exactly what dieters need,
And what discriminating bears prefer for their feed.

Skunked by Bureaucracy

Carolyn Greenwood

"Animal Control. Becky speaking."

"Hi Becky, Carolyn Greenwood here. I have a real problem. There's a skunk under my house and he's been there for about a week. He's spraying like crazy. We can even smell him inside the house two stories up! I have house guests coming. I don't know what to do!"

"Well, can he get out?"

"I don't know—I mean, I don't think so."

"If he got in, why can't he get out?"

"Well, I think my husband left one of the doors open overnight and he just crawled in."

"Well, then he can get out!" the voice pressed on.

"No, he can't get out because we closed the door."

She took a moment to respond. "I'm sorry, but I don't quite understand. If you want him to leave, why did you trap him inside by closing the door?"

"Well, uh, I guess we were worried that if he could leave, he might tell all his friends what a great place he's found and bring them all back, and then they'll all...." She interrupted me.

"Look, when skunks get frustrated, they spray. He's obviously upset because he can't get out. You need to open the door, lure him from under the house by making a trail of food leading to the outside, and get him away from your property. Once he's out, you close the door and your problem is solved."

She's got to be kidding, I thought. *My neighbors will love that.*

"You know I've never done this before. Could you please tell me, uh, what kind of food do skunks like to eat?"

"Peanut butter sandwiches seem to work," she responded.

"Hmm. Well, what if my trail of food attracts other skunks and leads them directly under my house?"

"Ma'am, I'm sorry—what was your name again?"

"Greenwood. Carolyn Greenwood."

"Ms. Greenwood, that is the risk you have to take. Now is there anything else I can do for you?"

"Uh, no. I mean yes. How far apart do I put these sandwiches?"

"Oh, three or four feet. Good luck. Goodbye."

"Uh, hold on just a minute. Don't you people send some-body out to—well—do something like bring traps to the house? Uh, my neighbor…." She interrupted me again.

"Ms. Greenwald," she enunciated distinctly, her voice rising, "we are two weeks backed up with requests for traps. We're very busy this time of year—you know, mating season and all that? I don't think you want to wait that…."

I interrupted her this time. "No, no, of course not, no." My voice dipped into a slump.

"Well, again, good luck," she chanted as from a memorized script.

"Yeees, uh, thank you," I muttered. She hung up. I stood looking at the receiver thinking, *Something is wrong here. How in the world am I ever going to catch him coming out his exit door so I can run to close it? I'd have to hide in the bushes like Inspector Clouseau twenty-four hours a day. What was she thinking of?*

I decided to borrow a trap from a neighbor. Then I made tiny tea sandwiches with peanut butter and jelly. I dutifully placed them three feet apart in a trail leading from under the house into the skunk trap that George had set down the hill.

Eureka! Within twenty-four hours I had my guy. I could hardly wait to call Animal Control to tell them about my success.

"Animal Control. Becky speaking."

"Hi, Becky. This is Carolyn Greenwood calling. I spoke to you day before yesterday." No response. "I'm the one who had the skunk under her house, guests com...."

"Okay, yes, sure, sure." She was good at interrupting. "What can I do for you today?"

"Well, guess what? I caught my skunk!"

Silence.

"How'd ya do that?" she finally exclaimed, her voice full of incredulity.

"Oh, I borrowed a neighbor's trap, used your idea of peanut butter canapés, and made a trail leading right into the trap. And voila! Caught him!"

"What do you plan to do now?" she asked with ice in her voice.

"Well, that's why I'm calling. I thought now you could come pick him up."

"Ms.—sorry—what was your name again?"

"Greenwood, just like redwood, only green."

"Ms. Greenwood, we don't pick up skunks that aren't caught in *our* traps."

"But I couldn't wait two weeks for your trap."

"I understand. But it is against our policy. We don't pick up skunks that aren't caught in our traps," she reiterated as if she were speaking to a child.

"What kind of silly rule is that? Never mind, don't answer. I don't want to hear it. Could you just please advise me what I'm supposed to do now?"

"You'll have to dispose of the skunk yourself."

"How do I do that?"

"The best way is to shoot it."

"What? Did you say shoot it? No, no, I don't think so. Do you have any other suggestions?"

"Some people drown them."

I gasped. "I don't think that will happen either." I felt like throwing up. "Excuse me," I said, "my husband is trying to tell me something. What? Poison? Oh, mercy, how about poison?"

"You'd never be able to buy a strong enough poison to kill an adult skunk," she reported.

"Isn't there some kind of medicine like Sominex that we could put in a sandwich that would put him to sleep? Then we could open the cage and he could be on his merry way."

"Ma'am, that is totally against the law. Once you trap a skunk, you cannot release him into the environment," she stated emphatically.

Suddenly a feeling of surrealism came over me, a dreamlike state where nothing made sense and I was not to worry because I would wake up soon and everything would be normal again. I didn't bother to ask her what purpose was behind that crazy law. I had had enough. After all, it wasn't her fault. I thanked her politely and hung up the phone.

I had another telephone call to make—to a government agency that also dealt with skunks.

I was still agitated when Bob answered the phone. I unloaded all my frustrations on him, even referring to myself as a desperate housewife—not the kind on TV but the kind who needed help with skunks. Bob chuckled at my diatribe.

I took advantage of his momentary good humor by asking, "Bob, can you help me dispose of this poor creature?"

Bob got serious. "You know I'm a very busy man. I cover the entire county of Calaveras. I have appointments coming out the kazoo for the next ten days for the explicit purpose of taking care of people just like you. How in the world am I supposed to help you when I'm booked? I don't understand why people don't use their heads before they trap an animal, like thinking about what happens afterwards!"

I couldn't respond.

He continued, "Apparently what you don't understand, Ms. Greenwood, is that you're supposed to call me *before* you trap your skunk, so I can tell you when I'll be in your area to take care of it. Does that make sense to you, Ms. Greenwood?"

"Oh, yes, absolutely. You're right, yes."

"Then, you see, you use *my* schedule for trapping your skunk. And I'm more than happy to come out and take care of it for you. Now do you see my dilemma? You have a skunk on your hands that's going to die a slow, painful death unless I come out very soon." He paused, sighed, took a deep breath, and asked, "Where do you live?"

I told him. He worked me in. Mr. Skunk went gently to skunk heaven. House guests arrived. All was well in the land of Greenwood. 🐾

Nearly Unbearable

Barbara Conrad

One of those perfect September weekends in the Mother Lode we headed in early morning to Calaveras Big Trees for a birthday celebration for our nine-year-old daughter. Her eight-year old sister joined in with enthusiasm.

The ranger at the entrance station took our money, gave us directions to both campgrounds, and warned us that the bears were active. That was not new to us. Calaveras bears are notorious.

"Have they hurt anyone?" I asked.

"Not since I've been here," he answered, "but one did step on the edge of a tent and surprised the heck out of a visitor."

I could handle that.

Our campsite had two levels—the car parked above and the tent site down several steps. A huge fallen tree provided a perfect headboard for our sleeping bags. "It's much too nice to sleep in the tent. Let's just lay our bags out here," I suggested. Everyone agreed. John and I settled our bags on each side of the girls'.

Since we were really roughing it, I cooked our breakfast right on the old park camp stove with bacon drippings slithering down the sides, toast burned just right by the flames, and eggs with overdone crinkled edges and underdone yolks. Later we hiked to the river with our books and camera. A perfect day in a perfect place.

Evening's campfire provided just the right ambience for lots of 'smores, storytelling, and birthday presents.

We hadn't been settled long in our bags before I heard the first bear noises far above us. We had complied with the park rules of leaving our garbage far up the hill, not locking our food cabinet, and not keeping any bear goodies in it. I listened as the park garbage can lids were tossed and the contents turned out for inspection. "Smoky" was getting closer and closer. People were yelling and banging on pans in efforts to steer him away.

Before many minutes scattered garbage littered the road above us and my heart beat a heavy, fearful rhythm. The hair rose on the back of my neck. John followed the bear's lumbering progress down the bank into our campsite with the flashlight. As the bear came closer, I stage-whispered to John, "You throw yourself on Stacey and I'll throw myself on Dana." We were prepared to save our children.

As it turned out, the bear's interest was not in our children but in our stove. He spent several moments licking the bacon grease off the sides. Loud snuffles amplified his enjoyment as he directed furtive glances toward the next campsite—never once taking notice of our presence.

As he worked his way from our campsite through others, cabinet doors ripped off, garbage cans upset, men yelled, and women screamed.

Morning brought scattered garbage, one very clean camp stove, and no one hurt. But ever after that I always cooked on my Coleman and slept in my tent—because I know ripstop nylon could deter any bear. 🐾

From My Window

Black Bird in the Morning

Jan Overstreet

The sun has finally risen;
Running a bit late this morning,
It hasn't helped dispel the
Grayness of the sky.

A few minutes ago
A tiny black bird zipped
Past my window, and lit
On one of the branches of
An oak.

A cat meanders
On the ground below.
I can almost see the
Bird's delight
In being safe
So high in the sky.

Silly Birds

Barbara Conrad

While my writing colleague, Jan, is relatively housebound and writing about chiaroscuro and patterns of tree branches outside her window, I'm seeing something quite different out my window.

Two very busy jays are setting up housekeeping. They have been buzzing in and out of my manzanita trying to break off small, dead branches to enhance their growing abode. They are also chasing every piece of string, paper, or fluff on the ground.

My two birds look identical. They are the same color all over, they both have small topknots of bright blue feathers, and they are the same size. Does that make them both males? Or females? Ornithology was never my long suit. Is this going to be an exercise in futility when they figure out that they are the wrong two to tango? In my biology classes we always learned that the male birds got the gorgeous plumage and that their mates were to be content with camouflage for protection and propagation of the species. I'm sure the Creator meant well, but we females have been trying to disavow this plan since time began.

As I sit at my dining room table and watch, I become more and more entranced with the construction project out my window. The birds have chosen a very large, tightly wound awning like those found on recreational vehicles.

If these are not gay birds, they are certainly beginners at nesting. So far the construction stretches from the top of the awning downward in a dangling three-foot mess. There is no way an egg would stay put anywhere in it. I keep telling the birds that sticks, even small ones, are probably not the best building material. And I don't think either one of them has a blazing IQ. They are quite unsuccessful in their attempts at ripping off small branches with their beaks. This is the time when folks feel sorry that birds don't have arms or fingers.

Now we are having a series of snows and I think that has changed their mind about spring nest building. Just this morning I noticed that he or she or both are moving the sticks from atop the big awning to a large nearby cedar tree. One hopes that the nest finally gets appropriately constructed, that they straighten out their sexuality, and that baby birds will grace our spring. 🕊

Squirrels

Gwen Serrière

Squirrel family,
they watch me from the oak trees,
scold me if I'm late.

Ah, sunflower seeds!
They'd sell their grey furry souls
for a handful more.

I've named two young ones
Rascal and Mischief—fits them,
their antics nonstop.

I learned to watch them
from my nature friend, Verna—
her soul is in them.

Missing Birds

Jan Overstreet

I'm looking out my windows
Now that the sun has finally
Come up. I am hoping to catch
Sight of the early birds
Swooping down for edible
Scraps left over from the
Poker party last night.
So far not one has appeared.

Well, it's Sunday, so I'll bet
They're sleeping late; maybe
Even birds enjoy
A day of rest.

Touched by a Dog

Retreat

Arlene Mueller

Both weigh in at 35 lbs.
Both stare at me with brown eyes.
One runs nonstop upright
The other prances on all fours.
Both beg me to play:
One whines, "NO, NO, thiisss way!"
The other tugs at my sock.
One sucks milk from a plastic cup
The other slurps water from a dish.
One loads his pants
The other poops in a snow pile.
One picks through my purse
The other chews on my tape recorder.
One never seems to sleep
The other claims half my bed.

I lock the bathroom door
against both of them.

Oliver Harris

Carolyn Greenwood

Dear Aunt Claire,

George and I are thrilled that you are coming to visit us in May. I need to tell you that we will have another house guest visiting at that time. Let me assure you that his presence won't interfere in the least with the activities we have planned for you. In fact, I know you will enjoy his company as much as we do.

His name is Oliver Harris. He's well mannered, handsome, and a joy to be around. Black as coal with deep brown eyes, he presents himself with a courtly elegance befitting his noble heritage. His walk is smooth and deliberate with the rhythm of an athlete. I tell you without exaggeration, Aunt Claire, he's really something to behold!

I do admit that sometimes Oliver displays an aloofness, especially when I have a bone to pick with him. As I begin to chide him, he turns his head and stares off into the distance as if to say, "When you are through boring me, I'll resume my day!"

Also I might add that although he blends well into our family, sometimes when we're all watching television I find him staring at me with his penetrating eyes. From his studied look, I suspect that he is actually checking out my lineage, my worthiness to have him in my life. But don't get me wrong, he's never deliberately rude. I think his behavior is bred into him from centuries past. He really believes that his status is above that of the common man—or any other animal for that matter.

His eyes are deep wells of mystery with a kind of melancholy that's rich in stories never to be told. When he wants attention but no one is taking heed, he stands upright, five feet tall, and gently places his arms on my shoulder, eyeball to eyeball, trying to express with his eyes what he can't with his mouth.

I must admit that he's the easiest house guest we've ever entertained. He eats the same boring thing every day. I pour two cups of dry mix from a bag and add a half cup of water. That's it!

However, last time he stayed with us he expressed an interest in artichokes. George and I were out on our deck enjoying the wonderful jumbo ones from the fields in Castroville when we noticed Ollie sitting upright, tail wagging, drooling. Until then we never fed him from the table, but this time I couldn't resist offering him a leaf. I demonstrated four or five times how he must not try to bite the leaf, but slide it through his teeth to get the luscious meat. At first he attempted to bite it hard. After I said *no* a few times and demonstrated again, saying, "Softly, like this, Ollie," he got the hang of it. I was never able to eat a whole artichoke again with Ollie around.

You know well, Aunt Claire, what a sports fan George is. Well, George and Oliver share the same interest. They love to play ball at Bret Harte Field, where George uses a tennis racket to hit the ball far and high in the air. Ollie takes off like a bullet, tracking the ball down the field, and then like Willie Mays, thrusts his body upward into a high leap and catches the ball, sometimes even over his shoulder! Oliver's athletic ability is so spectacular that people stop to watch his performance. The game goes on for forty hits and catches, which wears them both out.

Ollie also has another praiseworthy talent. And I know he indulges me when with a look of submissive resignation, he allows me to put a cookie on the end of his nose. He focuses alternately between the end of his nose and my hands as I back away. The cookie stays perched while he waits for the clap of my hands. Then he flips his head and the cookie flies up and lands in his waiting mouth. I often wonder if he subjects himself to this humiliation for the want of a cookie, or if it is the applause and praise he's after.

I must tell you that his toilet habits are beyond reproach. He pees and poops on command! Yes, he does! No matter what time of day. Armed with three doggie cookies, one for a pee and two for a poop, I take him to the designated place in our yard, to which I point and say, "Ollie *do!*" After sniffing for the perfect spot and doing a few circles in place, Ollie *does!*

What lesser behavior would you expect from an extraordinary seventy-five pound French poodle?

We look forward to your visit, dear aunt. Our friend Ollie is at his best when company arrives. We'll see you in May.

Love and best wishes,

Carolyn 🐾

Navajo Nomie and I

Lois Grisdale

While staying in Kayenta, Arizona, I took my usual evening walk with Linda and Art and their old basset hound. A neighbor's long-haired Border collie always joined us. I enjoyed seeing this young shaggy dog bounce and dance around us.

I loved the dry atmosphere and this wondrous, colorful desert with its outcropping of immense red rocks that rose out of nowhere to great height. We were following a sheep path in the sagebrush when Linda said, "The teacher where that dog stays is leaving the reservation and plans to take her own dog, not the Border collie. She considers him nothing but a stray. So why don't you take him?"

"What in heaven's name would I do with a dog?" I replied. "I don't even know where I'm going. I've just left a community in New Hampshire where I've lived for the past seven years. Everything I own is stored with friends in Santa Fe and I'll need to retrieve it in less than two months."

My stay in Arizona began when I traveled west in April 1993 and met Art and Linda. We attended a spiritual communal gathering held at a Navajo hogan (traditional home) in Slippery Rock. During our time together they invited me to stay in their house in Kayenta at the Navajo Government School where Art was a teacher. They wanted me to care for their old basset hound while they went rubber rafting down the Colorado River.

Upon their return Art said, "We have a friend, Jim, who wants to return to Ohio for his summer vacation and needs a house sitter for June and July." I met Jim and was delighted at the opportunity to care for his two-bedroom home.

The teacher who was leaving the reservation owned the immense brown dog she called Mack, probably because he was big and built like a truck. Mack was tied in front of her house on a long lead line and the black-and-white Border collie kept him company, but was free to roam. The Indian children called him Blackie and rode him like a horse.

A few days later Linda said, "You don't need to worry about the Border collie any longer for an Indian family has offered to take the dog." I was relieved.

In the last week of June I saw a small white truck parked in front of the teacher's house, but thought nothing of it since she was moving. That evening on our walk I missed the Border collie and asked Linda, "What's going on?"

"Oh, that truck was from Indian Animal Control. I think someone phoned them for they picked up the black dog and now he will be put down because he has no license."

I could not stand the thought of the dog being destroyed, so I decided to save him. I phoned Animal Control and learned their only office was in Many Farms, 50 miles away. When Linda heard of my plan, she offered to accompany me.

The next day we traveled across the hot desert landscape filled with amazing colors of orange, yellow, and red-purple-green outcroppings to Many Farms. The Animal Control office was difficult to find. Eventually we located a dirt road that led to a small structure under high wire towers out in the middle of nowhere. A small herd of goats, a few ducks, two pigs, a number of sheep, and a donkey wandered around outside the building. Inside sat three wooden chairs, a desk, and two metal file cabinets shoved together to make an office.

I paid for the Border collie's release, the cost of the rabies shot, and his stay of three days. While going through the transaction, the uniformed officer told us his amazing story of how he patrolled hundreds of acres of the reservation with only one assistant and on an extremely low budget. They handled sick sheep and rabid dogs and cared for all kinds of mistreated animals. My heart went out to this man and his job.

We entered a large room abutting the tiny office where the smell was strong and unpleasant, and cages held all kinds of animals. We retrieved the black dog and quickly drove back to Kayenta because of his odor.

Art helped us hold the animal as we soaped and scrubbed him to clean his coat. Now something unexpected was happening. I wanted to keep the dog. Knowing I had no place to live and my car would be loaded, I still wanted to keep him. I disliked the name Blackie so I decided to name him "No-Name" and began calling him Nomie.

Living with Nomie I've discovered he is terrified of guns. Hearing shots fired, he begins to tremble as he tries to hide. He is also leery of big men with deep voices. Perhaps because of this I suspect a man with a gun drove him off from where he lived. Later I learned Border collies that prefer the company of people do not make good sheep dogs.

That hot August of 1993 Nomie and I traveled west together. I kept a cold, wet scarf tied around his neck and a wet towel under him to keep him cool.

We settled in a cabin in the old gold mining countryside near Murphys where both of us have slowed down these past 12 years.

My friendship with Nomie has helped me realize parts of my own personality: my need to control and what makes me angry. I am upset when Nomie is told to come and stubbornly goes about his own business or chases the horses that pasture in the front field in an effort to protect me as we walk by.

I've come to appreciate Nomie's need for routine and have adjusted to his desire to warn me every hour of the cattle in the nearby hills. He always has accompanied me to the bathroom, a kind of reciprocity I've felt, for I go with him for his business, he mine. I'm not sure of his age though I think he is 13, and now he has arthritis and ear problems.

We have found a wonderful place to grow older together, a place where he can run, climb hills, and have dog friends. I have learned to appreciate his passion for daily walks that makes my life richer.

Sweet Basil's Eulogy

Yolanda Randlett

Sweet Basil is gone. Sadness fills my heart. My soul cries with anguish, and emptiness surrounds me. Even the sky mourns, covered with fog so thick it hangs heavy over our town. My home has lost a sparkling gem, and the loneliness cowers in corners that were once drenched with devotion.

Sweet Basil, our intelligent and loving border terrier for 15 years, often sat quietly, attentively watching everyone. She acted only when she felt someone was out of line or in trouble. We were all members of her pack—my husband and I and our other border terrier, Bravo.

One sunny California day Basil, Bravo, and I were enjoying a walk on the beach when we came upon a young man and his collie playing fetch with a rubber ball. Shagging balls was Bravo's passion and he joined the collie in the game. Basil ran, too, but her mission was to deflect the larger dog, allowing Bravo to retrieve the ball and drop it at the feet of the startled young man. Basil did not bark nor did she bully. She simply ran interference and somehow got the message across that the collie needed to forego the chase. He returned to his master and sat at his side, and there he stayed until the ball was thrown again. No encouragement would get him to budge. He watched as Bravo fetched the ball once more.

Basil was a wily hunter, quiet and cunning. On forest walks she stayed off the trails, running parallel to us, but seldom seen. Periodically I would get a glimpse of her.

She and Bravo would chase chipmunks into piles of wood slash. Bravo hunted with bluster, announcing to the world that he was on the prowl. Basil looked at him, showing disgust in her eyes. I could imagine what she would say if she could talk. But she used her guileless style to her advantage. He'd chase the chipmunks into the slash piles; she would run to the back, ready to catch them if they ran out.

On her last day our pack walked in the field behind our home. She moved slowly, stumbled, and fell, her little heart failing. My husband tried to leave us in the field and get the ATV to give her a ride. But she insisted on following him, so we carried her home. She was faithful to her pack to the end.

Later I saw Basil in a dream. She quietly sat at a gopher hole as she often had, strong and happy. I want to believe she came to let me know she was all right. It was so much in her character to be that considerate. I want to believe in a God to whom we all belong. I want to believe that she has returned to this spring of all life—maybe ready for another adventure, or maybe just patiently waiting for me. 🐾

Taffy, Unwanted

Jo Raye Doyle

I was raised on a small farm in the foothills of the Smokies. Dogs and cats, always kept outside, were a necessity: cats for mousing, dogs for hunting and chasing errant animals.

My husband, George, had an innate love for nature, especially trees, birds, animals, and all crawling things. He opened up a hidden dimension in my own life. From him I learned animal pets are a real source of love and companionship.

I was still lost in what, for me, was a new world. Instead of going off to teach daily I found myself with a new husband, a new home, and now a two-week-old colicky baby daughter, Sheila.

One day George brought home his thirteen-year-old son, Walter, to live with us. For months Walter had been chafing at the bit in a strict military academy where his mother, seeking help for this irascible one, had placed him soon after she and her husband had separated. Walter brought with him his six-week-old cocker puppy, Taffy, untrained and un-housebroken, of course. I realized that long before she was housebroken, my new house would be dog-broken. Walter, I had expected and could deal with, but the puppy was the straw that broke the camel's back.

In early mornings when Walter emerged from his room with Taffy, she immediately appropriated my new couch. It mattered not how many chairs, stools, and other odds and ends I placed on it to try to deter her, she managed to wriggle in and find a place for herself. I could hardly wait until Walter was off to school to relegate her to the backyard.

In the afternoons with Baby Sheila on a folded quilt at my feet, I tackled an overflowing basket of ironing. When Walter returned from school, ignoring the tail-wagging dog at the door, he went straight to the refrigerator. Returning with hands full of cookies and apples, still ignoring the begging dog, he also settled down at my feet. Finishing his food, he amused himself by stuffing one of Taffy's long ears in her mouth, closing her teeth down on it, and forcing her to bite it. I managed to ignore her cries, knowing he was only doing it to get a rise out of me.

On weekends and school vacations his mother allowed him to return to nearby West Covina to visit her, his three siblings, and his old community. He never took Taffy with him and she gradually became the family dog.

Taffy's one happy hour was when George returned home from work. Unable to contain her joy, she would tear back and forth from bedroom to kitchen while he divested himself of his business attire. Finally he relaxed at the kitchen table with his magazine and beer. Taffy, exhausted, lay contentedly at his feet.

Eventually she grew up. No matter how we tried to barricade the back gates and fence when she was in heat, one persistent little male cocker always got to her. When the puppies subsequently arrived, she paid them not the slightest attention. At night, especially, she would wander off into the far corners of the yard, leaving them alone in the doghouse. Their whimpering cries awakened me, but as soon as I took her back to her puppies and returned to my bed, she would leave them again.

Somehow they managed to grow up plump and adorable. Walter had no trouble finding good homes for them among his school friends. After that the vet took care of Taffy so we never had that aggravation again.

As Taffy aged, instead of losing her sight as many cockers do, she lost her mind. After many trips to the vet to remove extraneous objects—string, balloons, cardboard, plastic, paper, whatever—one day the vet suggested it was time to put her to sleep. Glad to be freed of her care, I readily agreed. I can't believe how completely self-centered I was, never once considering how Sheila and George might feel about this.

Sheila was away for a few days at scout camp at the time. She tells me now that when she came home, she was both sad and angry. Couldn't I have at least waited another week and given her a chance to say good-bye? No doubt her father, too, was very sad.

Recently I asked Sheila if she had any special memories of Taffy. She reminded me of three very special incidents that I had completely forgotten. I always fed Taffy on the back stoop just outside the kitchen door. When she had finished her food, she would ask to get back inside. One night I found her standing there holding her food bowl in her mouth, apparently indicating, "I do not eat in the rain." Sure enough a light rain was beginning to fall, so inside she came, deposited the food bowl in the corner, and ate there.

Also, she had an unusual way of amusing herself. Taking a small stone in her mouth, she would throw it and quickly catch it. I now wonder, was she needing someone to play with, to throw a ball or stick for her to fetch? This never occurred to us as we enjoyed watching her perform this strange feat with a pebble.

A third thing Sheila recalled is about Taffy's warm friendship with our mailman. She always met him at the corner. One day a new mailman, in fear, greeted her with a smart rap from a rolled up magazine. She never met him again. We tried to explain her love for the previous mailman. He replied, "I've been bitten by too many little dogs that do not bite."

Sometimes now I awaken all toasty and lie thinking of how lucky I am: good food, a warm bed, a caring family, and good friends. Then creeping around the corner of my mind will come a discomfiting memory of Taffy—the little dog I was not able to nurture. I certainly hope she is in a happier situation now. With any sense of justice in the scheme of things, she should be.

Etherden's Lady Guinevere

Jo Raye Doyle

After all the years I cared for the unwanted Taffy, we had only a mostly outside cat. He was not purposely kept out of the house, but seemed to go in and out as he pleased. He, too, loved my husband best. In daytime he stayed close to him as he worked in the yard. He grew up to be a nighttime prowler.

During his traditional nine lives, he survived badly infected wounds unseen under his long thick fur, strokes, and blindness because of glaucoma, which required daily medication. Otherwise he came and went as usual climbing over our backyard gate to be with my husband, George. Although he had been fixed by the vet to prevent his nightly brawls, he had grown to enjoy them so much he kept them up for years. Many times we had given him up and were just going to let him die in peace in his bed in the garage, when he would appear asking for food.

I unintentionally finished him off, also. One morning leaving my car running in the driveway, I hurried to close the heavy garage door. As always, it closed with a bang.

Sadly I learned from my family that he had strayed out of his bed and gotten just to the spot where the heavy banging door came down and hit him directly on the head!

The house was lonely without an animal family member. The family began to talk about getting a dog. In order that she not be another "unwanted," they carefully included me in all their plans. First, we read in our big National Geographic dog book and saw pictures of all the various breeds. We liked the Sealyham terrier and began to search the local papers for breeders' advertisements.

Shortly thereafter the three of us drove out to the San Fernando Valley and came home with Etherden's Lady Guinevere. The breeder's little smelly house was on a prize piece of property surrounded by the sprawling Howard Hughes Aircraft Company.

The jaunty elderly couple, the Etherdens, had photos, awards, and ribbons all over the place that the dogs they had bred had won. They watched approvingly as daughter Sheila lifted from the box of wriggling puppies the friendliest and most active one of the litter. "She will make a great show dog for you," the lady proclaimed. Only the ready money in hand persuaded them, with poor grace, to sell us the puppy we never meant to show. Her destiny was to be only a family pet.

Her responsibility was not mine. She immediately became at home in teenage Sheila's topsy-turvy room and bed. She loved us all, but especially played with Sheila. It was fun to see Sheila flat on the floor, her long hair completely obscuring her face with Gwennie running around her barking and snapping at her trying to find her face.

We all had fun throwing and bouncing a small rubber ball for her in the yard. No matter how high it bounced, with a great jump she would catch it in her mouth. "If you only had an arm," George often remarked, "the Dodgers would find you great at shortstop."

Among other duties she paid full attention to any family member who was slightly under the weather.

Stepson Dennis, now grown up and living many miles away, came back home to recuperate from a badly smashed ankle incurred in a motorcycle accident. Since stepson Walter was home at the time occupying our third bedroom, we had to set up a twin bed in the living room for Dennis. Gwennie immediately took up her post as nursemaid, staying close by all the weeks Dennis was there.

They became such friends that there developed a psychic bond between them. Even years later when many miles away, as Dennis would be thinking of an unannounced visit home, Gwennie would become very excited and station herself by the door waiting for him, refusing to budge until he appeared.

She dearly loved all of our family. Sometimes without informing her where we were going, we would turn right on Garfield Avenue on our way to see daughter Karin and her husband in Whittier. Though Gwennie often was in the car when we turned in the same place on other errands, she seemed to know this time it was to visit Karin and Vern. All the ten-mile drive, she hardly could contain her joy. Once inside their lovely little carefully kept house, her decorum was such that it was always a pleasant visit.

As Gwennie grew older she began to have a bad reaction to the groomer's tranquility pill—George bought a dog's barber kit and became the groomer. Gwennie never looked quite as elegant, but we were all happier.

In the summer when I went to see my aged mother in Tennessee for a few days, we always used to take Gwennie back to the Etherden's for care. One time on picking her up we found her covered with fleas; this made us realize that the aging Etherdens could no longer be depended on. We started looking for a place where she would receive good care. We found such a place. We left her there for a weekend so she would get acquainted and would know on a longer visit that we would be returning for her.

On the eve of our leaving for Tennessee, to our dismay, we found she was inhabited with a multitude of ringworms. Such expert instructions from the vet concerning her care were given to us that George, realizing the opportunity to avoid that week or so in hot, humid East Tennessee, volunteered to stay home and care for Gwennie. She found the house too quiet without us. When we phoned, George said our voices would animate her for a bit before she returned to her bored waiting for our return.

Across the years she developed a very painful digestive disorder. After eating she would tear frantically up and down the yard trying to alleviate the pain. The vet-prescribed tranquility pill only added to her discomfort. Finally, a young friend brought me some marijuana to try. About half an hour before mealtime she quickly ate the crushed dry leaves from my hand. For a while that helped so much that I became an advocate for its use on people. I have no patience with the stuffed shirts who would deny it to the many suffering dying people whose lives it could enhance so much.

Eventually as time wore on even marijuana did not help. At night we had to close her in the kitchen and every morning I had to spend my first hour on arising bathing her and the kitchen floor. It was not right to let her continue to suffer so.

George had to go to an innovative Long Beach surgeon for needed hernia surgery. Of course he came first. Gwennie must be put down. That morning for the first time in ages Gwennie appeared at George's side asking for her bite of toast. The reluctant vet remarked, "Her little heart is so strong." He had never seen the resulting ravages of her misery.

So the few days it took George to recover from his surgery, I felt with a tearful aching heart that I had murdered my child.

Sealyhams in this country have become almost extinct. A few years later when we saw one of the comic little fellows on a leash in a northern redwood park, our delight was tempered by memories of our own little Gwennie, whose last days had been so misery-filled, yet her earlier years had been such a joy to us all. She had enriched all our lives. 🐾

Lee's Guardian

Marian Cramer

My older sister, Lee, had a guard dog, a German shepherd named Laddie. Grandfather Ballard brought Laddie into our family as a gift when Lee began to walk, and she learned to toddle with Laddie at her side. No one ever told him he was her watchdog, he just knew it. I grew up hearing "Laddie, the Guard Dog" stories.

Whenever Lee and Mother went for a walk, Laddie walked, too. Neighbors would stop and chat with Mother and even smile at Lee. They soon learned that Lee could be talked to and smiled at, but never touched. An outstretched hand to gently pat Lee's happy face brought a frightening bark as Laddie placed himself in front of Lee, quickly fending off the would-be patter.

Mother confessed to feeling very much at ease with this diligent babysitter on duty. He not only kept a wary eye on anyone who approached Lee, he also had an instinct to bark and bring mother running if Lee were about to climb up or slide down a dangerous spot. He kept her in the yard with his constant vigilance and barked ferociously if she rode her tricycle past a certain point in the driveway. Sometimes he gently nudged her or blocked her way, but he knew it was his job to protect her and he did. Mother was always close by, of course, but Laddie saved her many a step by herding Lee to safety in a timely way.

He was always on duty. Lee recalled to me his habit of keeping her in bed if she woke before the household did. He would lie beside her bed, and if she put one foot over the edge, Laddie nudged it back on the bed with his nose. She told me she never feared him, but she did know who was in charge.

One dramatic day when Lee was old enough to run, she headed down the driveway chasing a ball. Mother was screaming, "Lee, Lee, stop!" as she flew after her heedless daughter. Before Lee reached the curb, Laddie grabbed her skirt with his teeth, and without so much as touching her skin, pulled her back. I heard this exciting rescue story often. So did everyone else we knew. Laddie was a genuine hero. Everyone loved him.

Children walking home from school also learned about Laddie. He would lie quietly on our lawn as the kids marched along chatting with each other. However, the day came when Lee teased one of the boys, who then came in the yard and gave her a push. Exactly what Lee said was never part of the story. Laddie put both front paws on the boy's shoulders and barked in his face in a no-nonsense tone. Mother ordered Laddie to sit and scurried down the porch stairs to reassure the frightened students, but saw only the backs of fleeing sweaters and jackets. After that, the school children walked home on the other side of the street.

Somewhere along the way, I was born. If there were ever a Laddie and Marian story, I never heard it. I've never seen a picture of Laddie and me together. I have no memory of this dog except in oft-told tales of his valiant ways with Lee. As a young girl, I often wished he had been *my* guard dog, too.

As a young adult, I began to ask why I was not in the pictures or the stories. It is realistic to believe Laddie did not welcome a new toddler into his territory. When I was old enough to ask what had happened to the Laddie of so many tales, the answer was never quite the same. He got sick or was poisoned or ran away. I still don't know where he went or when. My real question was simply, "Why?" This haunting question lingers, unanswered. Like small children everywhere, I was certain it had been my fault.

I have never owned a dog, or wanted to. I experience terror at the first clink of a dog collar chain—or worse—a barking challenge. Not dislike, or just a little afraid. I am petrified into full-blown panic. Heart-pounding, adrenalin-rushing, paralyzing hysteria. My fear predates my earliest memories. I have studied my body for telltale marks of canine teeth. There are none, but my fear scars are profoundly visible. No one in my family claims to know why.

I continue to ponder why a three-year-old little girl would suffer such inner fear of all creatures canine. What terrifying scene seared my young brain that demonizes every dog I'll ever see? Instinct tells me that perhaps Laddie knew. 🐾

Pandora's Box, Gift-wrapped

Grace Muirhead

Under the Christmas tree was a box that bulged first this way, then that. It emitted raspy sounds. And it was for *me!* From my boyfriend!

Earlier I had asked Sis if she knew what Tom was planning to give me that year when I was eighteen. Yes, she knew, she said, but she wouldn't tell me what the gift was.

"Well, how much should I spend on Tom's present?" I asked, trying cagily to get more information out of her.

"A lot," came her unwelcome reply.

On Christmas morning, Mom, Dad, Sis, and I opened gift after gift, always aware of the scritch-scratch emanating from the large-ish, beautifully wrapped package that Tom had delivered before I was awake. It sat slightly apart from the mound of crumpled paper we had tossed aside as we opened one surprise after another. At last the moment arrived when no unwrapped packages awaited anyone any more. No packages, that is, except for the animated one.

"Can't avoid it any longer, Grace," Dad said, shoving the box my way. "Let's see what this is all about."

I was all too afraid I already *knew* what it was all about. Such a lively container could mean only one thing. So I pulled the ribbon off as slowly as I could, then slid my fingernail carefully under each patch of tape to prolong the moment of truth as long as possible. I seemed to have help from inside the box as I lifted the lid.

As I feared, out sprang a small, scared, excited puppy. A beagle puppy! Wearing a red ribbon and a bell. A beagle puppy so nervous that she introduced herself by creating a small, yellow puddle that was soon absorbed by the living room rug. A beagle puppy that immediately created a Christmas like none before in our household. A puppy that peed often and indiscriminately, that chewed on the chairs, the Christmas tree, and everything in between. A puppy that howled all night, every night, no matter the ticking clock, hot water bottle, and soft blanket in her paper-lined box next to my bed. No matter that I dangled my limp but unrested hand so that it touched her. A puppy, in short, that no one wanted and that no one was even slightly prepared to live with!

As our lives reverted to the normal post-Christmas routine, the puppy lived in the basement during the day. Mom and Dad both went off to work, Sis to high school, and I to college. After classes I routinely headed straight downstairs upon coming home. I threw a ball for the eager little beagle and pretended to enjoy it as much as she did. I let her outside with the feeble hope that this would house-train her. (This, Tom's mother told him after she'd happened to see the puppy in the snow outside our house one day, was a cruel thing to do in the Arctic-like winters of Wisconsin.) After I let my unwelcome gift back into the house, I would do my best to study on the basement's bottom stair. Tough to do with an energetic dervish leaping onto the books and chewing the pages. Sometimes I tried knitting the sweater for Tom that I had started during my intolerably boring econ lectures. Even tougher to do. Puppies, like kittens, seem prone to attacking skeins of yarn as though they are mortal enemies.

Things got intolerably bad when Mom came home from work. For some reason, that always set the beagle off, and how she howled! Mom's temperament did not accept competition in the howling department. Besides, she had ulcers at the time. The afternoon, some time in January, when she hurled a bottle of baby food, her ulcer diet, down the stairwell at my pet and me, did the trick.

Dad did the manly thing. He called Tom, put the puppy and lots of newspaper in the car, and drove to Tom's house. Never again, he told Tom in so many words, give such a gift, no matter how cute, to any member of our family or to anyone in our immediate neighborhood. The puppy, I assume, went back to the breeder where Tom had found it.

Sis at last divulged a bit more information about why the dog arrived as a Christmas gift, the dog who never had a name. Tom wanted to find out if I'd make a good mother. Perhaps his discovery that I wasn't ready for that stage of life is why he broke up with me shortly after I gave him his hand-knit sweater. 🐾

The Tale of Molly

Jo Raye Doyle

When Sheila, my daughter, found Molly, our beautiful golden lab and shar-pei mix, she was in a Jackson animal shelter. Sheila had gone there at the end of her work day at Bret Harte High School, hoping to find a companion for Spike, our lovely black lab who had been moping around spiritless since her delightful playmate Cindy-Lou had died of cancer.

As Sheila went down the line of cage-like boxes, Molly, at the very end, apparently recognizing a kindred soul, kept calling to her as if she were saying, "Don't choose yet, I've been waiting for you."

Once in the car with her, Sheila immediately gave her a new name—Molly. No longer was she Bumper, the name her keepers had given her as they anxiously watched her become bigger and bigger. Seems all takers at the shelter were looking for younger dogs nearer the puppy stage. Obviously becoming emotionally attached to her, they were so glad to find someone who really wanted her.

Up to this point her life had been somewhat disappointing. She watched longingly as others in her litter had been led away by satisfied owners. An older woman who wanted her had pled with the shelter people to keep her a bit longer, and finally after weeks of waiting she came and took her happily to a real home.

Sometime afterward, she was returned, the old woman whining, "I can't keep her, she chases my cat!"

Arriving at the Doyle-Lortz ménage at dark, there was barely time for Molly to greet Spike, have her dinner, and collapse in the doggie bed awaiting her.

Early the next morning Spike, who in the lonely interim had been going in the truck with Charlie, the daddy, off to work, jumped in his truck with Sheila and Chris, who were off to school. Charlie unceremoniously dumped Molly with me.

Rejected again, she must have thought and immediately started demolishing my little house.

First, my little Lucy Dog's stuffed toys, torn and bedraggled, were strewn all over. Next the overstuffed chair and the couch corners were tackled ferociously.

Trying in vain to quiet her rampage with soothing talk and innumerable dog biscuits, I soon found myself with papers and towels picking up and cleaning up huge piles and puddles of dog poop all over the house.

Watching me with more or less disdain, she finally collapsed on Lucy's special rug in the broom closet. The remainder of the day I couldn't have asked for a more amenable companion.

"I'll have to take her back," Sheila said, after coming for her at the end of the day and listening to my story.

"Oh, no," I insisted, "she'll be just fine with her new family all home for the weekend." Like the shelter people, I had quite fallen in love with her. And I was right, because after that first disappointing day she settled in and things went along swimmingly, we thought, until one day after her morning romp over the hill with Spike and a neighbor dog, she came home carrying in her mouth a bloody, half-eaten hen. Charlie learned from our patient dog-loving neighbor that this was her eighth victim.

What to do? Somebody said to tie the bloody remains around her neck and make her wear that a full day. That would teach her. We couldn't quite bear this, so after a short while we removed the bloody hen. Fearful Molly's marauding ways would continue, Sheila contacted an animal psychic. The helpful woman immediately guessed Molly's trouble. "She is afraid! She doesn't know yet that she at last has a real loving home. She just thinks that any moment she'll be rejected again." Lastly she said, "I'm going to pray for her," which we all did. Eventually Molly again seemed happy, obedient, and secure, using her boundless energy wrestling and playing with Spike, especially in the mornings.

One morning as Charlie started off to work, maneuvering his truck slowly and carefully to avoid the playing dogs who usually were also careful to stay out of his path, he heard a terrified yelp. Stopping quickly he found Molly, her tail pinned under a wheel. She was mangling it completely struggling to free herself. Apparently Spike, in his exuberance, had suddenly given her a powerful body slam right under the wheels of the moving truck.

Sorrowfully the kindly vet was forced to amputate a goodly portion of that lovely, heavy tail. Surprisingly Molly, no longer feeling the heavy drag of her tail, learned for the first time that a tail is to wag.

Since that time she has been wagging it so joyfully that at least the back half of her body wags with it. In fact she has become the embodiment of that old adage, "The tail wags the dog."

Dog School Dropout: a Children's Story

Grace Muirhead

Otto is handsome. His coat shines, he smells good, and his manners are almost perfect. He even seems to smile when he wags his tail at us. Wags his tail? Well, why not? Otto's a dog—a black Labrador retriever who lives across the street with Bart and Pam.

Everyone in our Forest Meadows neighborhood loves him. In fact, Jim, who lives next door, keeps a supply of dog treats in his garage so he can feed Otto whenever he and Bart stop by on one of their frequent walks.

But Otto wears a mysterious tag on his collar. It says, "I am proud to be a career change dog from Guide Dogs for the Blind." Now why would that be?

When we first met Otto, he was a squirmy, whiny little black bundle of energy and affection. He wiggled all over when we approached him. He jumped up as high as he could to greet us, and he'd lick our hands and faces if we bent down to pet him. That always made me giggle.

Bart took him wherever he was going: to the store, to restaurants, to church, to the golf course, for long walks, and oh! so many other places. And whenever Otto went away from home, he wore a special jacket, just his size. As Otto grew bigger, Bart and Pam got new, larger jackets for him—three in all. No matter what size they were, they were bright green. And printed on them in white letters was "Puppy in training for Guide Dogs for the Blind."

For Otto was being "socialized" at Bart and Pam's house so he could do a big job when he grew up. He was going to be a guide dog for a person who could not see. He would wear a special harness and undergo very difficult and demanding training.

In the meantime, all of us lucky people in the neighborhood and about town grew to know and enjoy Otto. He always made us happy to see him. And when we came across him at the drug store, we felt proud of what he would become one day.

When Otto was still very young, but already big and strong, Bart had a hard time keeping him from jumping up on people. Bart didn't want him to make someone fall down! Otto was just too excited about everything he came across, be it a person, a butterfly, or another dog. Once, when Otto was still a puppy, but quite large, Bart and Pam entertained people who brought a small, pesky beagle puppy with them. The puppy nipped at Otto's paws and jaw mercilessly, trying to get him to play. The puppy climbed all over Otto. When Otto tired of all the bother, he merely placed his large paw on the puppy, which calmed the little fellow right down. Otto never snarled or snapped. He was kind and patient.

Well, Otto got to be a year old or so, and off he went to San Rafael where he would take lessons that would teach him exactly how to behave when he became the "eyes" for a blind person. All of us, especially Bart and Pam, were sad to see him go, but we knew what an important job was in store for Otto. That helped us to be just a little happy.

Otto was gone for quite a while. Jake, the springer spaniel down the street, probably missed him as much as we did, but of course we couldn't tell. Jake and Otto had romped together through the neighborhood. They had run wild circles around each other. They had chased each other back and forth until they collapsed into two panting heaps of fur. Without Otto around, Jake hardly ran at all. Did we just imagine it, or did his face droop a little – just enough so that it looked sad?

One day much later, we saw Bart taking his usual walk, and there was a dog with him. *Could it be?* we wondered. *Could it be Otto?* As we came closer, it was clear. Otto was back! Oh happy day!

But why did he come back?

Bart shook his head as he told us the story. "Otto's training consisted of nine steps. When the trainers from San Rafael called to tell us how Otto was doing, at first they always said that Otto was an outstanding trainee. In fact," Bart declared proudly, "he was the only puppy in training who managed to complete an obstacle course that required him to climb ladders, jump off high platforms, balance on narrow planks of wood, and many more difficult maneuvers. And once, when we visited him during the training, the trainer put a blindfold on me and instructed Otto to guide me through a maze. Otto managed to do it perfectly!"

So Otto had made it through seven of the nine steps toward becoming an official guide dog.

During all this training, he had encountered lots of other dogs—including a dog who attacked him. Even though Otto had gashes on his paw and his ear, he didn't fight back.

"The one thing Otto couldn't manage to do was to stop paying attention to the other dogs. He wanted to be friends with all of them, even the one who attacked him." That, according to Bart, was why Otto is back in Forest Meadows instead of helping a blind person. "Evidently," Bart said, "if a dog in training becomes distracted, he might not pay enough attention while leading someone across a busy street. Now that would be a bad thing!"

So the trainers at Guide Dogs for the Blind decided that Otto just wasn't meant to be a guide dog. That didn't mean that Otto wouldn't be a wonderful pet for someone, though, so they called Bart and Pam. "Do you want him back?" they asked.

Well, of course they answered, "Yes! Yes, yes, yes!"

But Bart and Pam are just a little bit sorry that Otto will never wear the official harness and perform the official duties he was bred to do. Instead, he proudly sports his new collar tag and brings joy to all of us who watched him grow up. We're glad he's back! 🐾

Guide Dogs for the Blind Training Steps

Grace Muirhead

The first seven training exercises are what Otto mastered during his schooling at Guide Dogs for the Blind. Can you believe that Otto, or any dog, could be so smart?

STEP 1 The dog learns to wear a harness and learns several commands such as "forward," "halt," "hop up," and "steady." The trainer introduces him to distractions like toys, food, other dogs, and cats that the dog needs to ignore when he is in harness.

STEP 2 The harness training continues. The dog practices in quiet residential areas and malls, and rides in training vans. He practices at curbs and street crossings and on an obstacle course. He learns some new commands and responses such as "right," "left," and "over here." And he has social sessions with other dogs.

STEP 3 The dog moves on to busier sections of town and more difficult curbs and street crossings. He starts to guide the instructor through an obstacle course and learns to be aware of clearance heights. And the instructor sees how the dog reacts to head collars.

STEP 4 The instructor is blindfolded while the dog guides her. The dog also learns how to guide people through pedestrian traffic, up and down stairs, and on different kinds of surfaces.

STEP 5 The dog learns to function in heavy pedestrian and vehicle traffic areas, and areas without sidewalks and with rounded curbs. He learns how to do turns while he is moving. Besides all this, he learns "intelligent disobedience." This means he refuses to obey a command if it is unsafe to do so.

STEP 6 The instructor now takes the dog into very challenging situations such as downtown San Francisco, bus-riding, light-rail riding, and platform edges. She also introduces the dog to low overhead clearances, off-leash obedience, and how to behave in heavy traffic.

STEP 7 The dog trains in crowded indoor malls and on slick floors and escalators. There is more advanced sidewalk training with obstacles.

STEP 8 Now it's time for final obedience testing. This includes on-leash obedience with the instructor wearing a blindfold, off-leash obedience, response to distractions, and final traffic testing. Then the dog guides novice or unfamiliar handlers.

STEP 9 This last step is final guidework testing. The dog and his blindfolded handler must cover a 40- to 50-minute route that tests every aspect of guidework, plus a repeat of obedience testing.

Near the Barnyard

The Day after Thanksgiving

Arlene Mueller

I drive past the turkey barracks
yards cleared, windows covered
where last summer chicks swarmed
pushing against the wire fences
where today only feathers
white wisps
cling like dandelion fuzz
to dead grasses waiting
for winter rains to wash
them away
removing all warnings
to the next unsuspecting chicks.

The Damn Bay

Faye Morrison

"It was The Bay, wasn't it? The damn bay," teen-aged Bob asked one more time, his eyes actually focusing for a moment.

His worried mother looked down at him sprawling across his bed. "Yes, Bob, you were thrown from your bay horse. Dr. Floreth says you'll be okay," she answered, trying to sound more convinced than she felt.

The doctor had actually said, "He'll probably snap out of this concussion-related amnesia in a few hours," mistakenly thinking that *probably* was a reassuring word. Bob's eyes dulled again, and he moved restlessly, moaning a bit as his bruised body reacted painfully to any tensing of muscles.

Bob had been on the local race track that August afternoon with his gelding, a never-named horse the family always referred to as "The Bay," which describes a horse of sorrel coloring with black mane and tail. Galloping around the homestretch, The Bay was evidently startled when a loose paper blew under his feet, and, according to witnesses, he shied violently to one side—and Bob went straight ahead. Bob was always careful when riding The Bay because he was a mount on the wild side. Bob expected him to buck at the beginning of a ride, perhaps even after supposedly settling down. But Bob didn't expect this sudden veering in the midst of a run; unprepared, he flew off the horse onto the dusty track.

Spectators rushed to his aid, relieved when he was able to pull himself into a sitting position. Dirtied and bleeding, obviously shaken, Bob still was able to grin when asked if he was all right. "Sure," he said, though wincing from pain, "I have to be all right. I have a date tonight."

When a volunteer driver got Bob to the doctor, he wasn't feeling so jaunty. He hurt all over and felt woozy. Though he never quite passed out, his answers to questions got more and more vague and his memory of what had happened disappeared entirely. By the time his mother arrived, the doctor said he had a concussion, many abrasions and bruises, but no broken bones. "It's okay, Bernice," the doctor assured his patient's mother, "Bob's probably going to snap out of this...."

Back at home, Bob's mother helped him up the stairs to his room, where he sighed with relief as he sank down on his bed. She fussed over him, torn between worry and anger that his father had ever let him ride The Bay. *Homer knows that horse is unreliable. He should never have bought him, a cheap horse because he threw and hurt his last owner! Both Homer and Bob are just plain daft over that blasted horse!*

"It was The Bay, wasn't it? The damn bay," Bob fretted again. This time his eyes remained unfocused and he didn't really wait for an answer, just closed his eyes, stretched out, and breathed deeply.

Later, younger sister Faye poked her nose in the bedroom door to announce that the acquaintance who had driven Bob to the doctor was downstairs asking about him. "Bring John up," Mother said.

And John looked in on the battered boy. "You're in no shape for a heavy date, Bob," he quipped.

Date? This was the first the family had heard of it and Bob looked totally confused. He didn't remember any date, and his harried mother assigned the puzzle to Faye. "Find out who Bob's supposed to go out with, and cancel it."

Faye dithered about what she should do, where to start. Bob's long on-again, off-again romance with Maxine was currently off, so she wasn't the one to be called. Faye half-heartedly called a couple of girls in Bob's class, but she felt foolish asking these older girls if they were dating her brother, and telling them, "If so, forget it, he's a mess!"

As early evening closed in, Bob's dad, Homer, arrived home from the ranch and looked at his beat-up son with consternation. Bob was still muttering about The Bay, but didn't seem able to carry on a sustained conversation. Homer shook his head and went about his usual routine; *denial* was his only defense when a family member seemed vulnerable to real hurt. *Maybe I shouldn't have encouraged Bob to ride The Bay,* he thought, *but horseback challenges are better than a lot of other risky teen behavior.*

Somehow between numerous trips up and down the stairs checking on Bob, his mother managed to prepare a simple meal, which Bob ate with his usual appetite, but his head was still muddled, and he asked over and over what had happened. Bob had been fascinated with the bay horse since his dad had bought him. The horse was skittish and unreliable…sort of a rogue— traits Bob yearned to try out himself but couldn't combine with being a good student and a semi-dutiful son.

Sometime after dinner and another conversation with the still calm and comforting doctor, Bob's mother answered yet one more phone call. In a small town in the 1940s, information traveled fast and concerned friends and relatives kept checking on how Bob was doing. This call, however, came from teen-aged June, a cute blonde family friend who lived way across town and somehow hadn't heard the news. "Where in the devil is Bob?" she asked his mother. "He was supposed to take me to the movies."

Shortly afterward, a still-startled June walked in the door and joined the family in the worried vigil. Minutes turned into more than an hour and Bob seemed sometimes better, then not. About 9:30 a siren pierced the soft darkness of the summer night. His mother's face stiffened and war-induced panic flooded through her. "Not an air raid warning on top of everything else!"

Bob, now sitting up, looked over at his worried mother and said in his normal voice, "It's okay, Mom. That's just a fire, not an air raid warning."

And, suddenly, the frightening ordeal was over. Bob was okay; his eyes focused and his mind worked. He never did recall the hours between galloping on the horse and the sound of the siren, but he recovered to have many more movie dates and continued to be intrigued and challenged by his wild bay horse. 🐾

Potbellied Persistence

Marlene Wiley Bradford

Max, our Welsh corgi, and I took our usual walk down to the bottom of our hill on a breezy warm October afternoon amid colorful falling leaves. We were surprised to see a small potbellied pig feeding on acorns under one of the large old live oak trees, in a golden field of dry grass. Max bristled when he saw the pig. I pulled gently on his leash and said quietly to him, "No bark—she's a nice little pig—be quiet."

Max looked from me to the pig, who came closer, eyeing us curiously, turning her head from side to side. Then she ran back under the tree and continued to root among the acorns. We saw her often after that. Neighbors began to speak of the pig. No one knew where she had come from, nor could anyone get close to her.

While driving to and from town, I often saw her under trees in the area, and sometimes standing among horses in their pastures, near the small winery. When our fall days became rainy, the pig protected herself from the storms by standing underneath one of the horses.

Max and I wandered past the winery on a chilly November morning. We stopped at the barbed-wire fence where three horses were pastured. The pig stood next to a gelding, who lowered his head and sniffed her as she made soft grunting sounds. Then the pig ran toward an old gray nag, who was lying

down. The third horse, a filly, walked over to stand between the nag and the pig. The filly lifted one hoof, moving it back and forth in front of the pig, to ward her off. As the little pig circled the nag, the filly stayed between the two animals, and then made threatening gestures with her head.

The old horse, having had enough of the pig's harassment, shakily stood and walked away, while the pig sauntered over and urinated on the spot where she had been lying. Then she grunted a few times in a loud boastful manner.

I was amazed to see what happened next. The pig reversed her direction and went back to the gelding, who began nibbling along her back. The pig again made contented grunting sounds, while the horse's soft lips continued nibbling. When the gelding lifted his head to look around, the pig stood on her hind legs, placing her front feet against the horse, reaching up toward his shoulder. She stood in that position for a few minutes, then lowered herself to the ground. The horse began nibbling on the pig's back again, continuing to pacify her.

I patted Max and gently pulled on his leash. He stood up, and we walked toward home. "I told you she was a nice little pig," I said, "but I'm beginning to think she's pretty self-centered."

We saw her now and then until the weather turned cold. I missed her and wondered where she was eating and sleeping. Rain washed summer dust from the horses' coats, and they gleamed in the winter sun. As deciduous trees afforded winter views, I continued to look for the pig. She never came back. 🐾

Mud Wrestling

Jane Lang

Bloodcurdling human-like screams permeated the air one quiet Sunday afternoon, interrupting my nap in the swing on the front deck. The distressing sounds continued as I jumped up to call my husband, Carroll. "Someone's in trouble," I yelled. "We've got to do something. The sounds are coming from Phil's pasture. I know he isn't home. You go over. I'll be right behind you when I find my shoes." I rushed into the house, passing Carroll as he headed out the door.

"Don't panic, Janie. We'll go see what's going on." My patient, loving husband moved purposefully out the door and down the steps to a gate opening to the neighbor's field. I caught up with him as he reached the enclosed area by the barn where the shrieks continued.

He climbed cautiously under the electric fence into a muddy enclosure. I held my breath as I crawled after him, certain I would be electrocuted. Searching around the pen, Carroll pointed to what appeared to be a large flesh-colored rock. Moving closer, he spotted a blond curly tail attached to a large rump huddled in a corner. Even though at first glance it had appeared to be a rock, the source of the racket had a snout and small beady eyes, and a body writhing in pain.

A pig, weighing at least 250 pounds, was tethered to the fence by a horse-like halter with rings. He had entrapped his hoof in one of the rings, causing his leg to swell like a balloon.

The pig repeated the piercing scream followed by snorts and grunts, foam dribbling from his mouth. He was in misery, and guess who would have to release the ring from his leg? Not me, but Carroll.

On his hands and knees assessing the situation, he proceeded to bark orders. "You have to hold his back legs so I can somehow force the ring from his swollen left front hoof. I know you can do it, but it won't be easy. Just be sure you don't let go. I know pigs have a powerful kick, so for goodness sake hang on." Glancing at the frantic look on my face, he added, "Remember, you can't let go."

When I grabbed the two slimy back legs, the pig, with renewed strength, kicked so hard I nearly toppled over. "Hurry up! I can't hold his legs much longer, Carroll. He's really strong." I gritted my teeth, the perspiration dripping down my face, barely able to keep a tight hold. The pig suddenly defecated on both of us. The smell nearly gagged me. My hands and arms ached, but somehow I hung on as Carroll continued to work to force the ring over the pig's hoof.

The stressed beast then relieved himself by directing a steady spray of urine on Carroll's face. Carroll was so incensed he pushed as hard as he could and released the ring from the victim's leg.

The pig, relieved in more ways than one, rolled over on his side, burrowed in the mud, and went into a deep sleep. He didn't move even when we touched the injured leg to determine if it was broken.

Both Carroll and I felt like a pair of defeated fighters, covered with mud, urine, and excrement, our hands and arms blue from bruises inflicted by the feisty animal. I glanced over at the sleeping swine and muttered under my breath as I flicked a glob of mud at his face, "Here's mud in your eye, you ungrateful beast!"

Stuffed with Love

Loss

Arlene Mueller

Peter wakes up halfway home
—cries Bear! Where's Bear?
I stop, search the car seat,
floor, cushions.

"Don't cry, we'll go look for Bear!"

At the beach, Peter whimpering
in my arms, we follow the flashlight
scanning for a furry face or paw,
finding only a blanket of empty sand.

"Yes, I know you want Bear.
I want Bear, too.
Maybe Bear's gone on a trip...."

As Peter's sobbing lessens, he nods off.
I ease into steady traffic, knowing
tomorrow my little guy and I will
wake to an empty world.

Toying with Memories

Barbara Conrad

"You can't know how embarrassed she was. You really can't," Zippy spoke to his silent shelf buddy, Peaches. "She could have melted, right down to her seal-point paws."

Peaches nodded and waited for the rest of the story. They had stood together on the top shelf of the bookcase for several years. Childhood toys of this family.

"I was used to being dragged all over the house; after all, John loved me best of all his toys. And when I was new, there was no better looking toy dog in the store. I had velvety brown fur perfect for petting, soft brown eyes, and I could be pulled around because I stood on wheels. Young John would drag me all around the neighborhood, and when the family moved, I was always there with them.

"Well, things changed when John grew up, went to college, and then got married. I didn't get to go along. John's mother stuck me in a box along with his tin soldiers and his Cub Scout uniform. I was chagrined, to say the least."

Peaches nodded in commiseration.

"One day many years later, John's mother came and got me out of the box, tied a new string to my collar, and brushed up my fur. My wheels worked just fine even though there wasn't much paint on them anymore. Was I one happy 12-inch dog!"

Peaches yawned in agreement.

"Little did I know that John had daughters and that John's mother was going to let them play with me. The girls pulled me up and down the long hall and swung me around the corner by the kitchen—and even dragged me around the patio. I felt like my old self. Well, sort of like my old self. I didn't much appreciate being dressed up in frilly doll clothes. But I had fun with the girls."

Peaches turned her one good eye to Zippy and seemed to smile.

Zippy continued, "Sometimes John's mother would just let me sit in the hall to wait until the girls came again. It was fun being part of the family once more. Peaches, didn't you have fun with John's wife when she was a little girl?"

Peaches replied, "We didn't do too much together except hug. Sometimes she got me all wet when she cried all over me. But I was a pretty dog, too. I got to be in Barbara's one-year-old photograph, and I was shiny and had both eyes then."

Zippy nodded appreciatively and continued, "I really looked forward to those Sundays when John and Barbara would bring the girls to play with me. But one Sunday they came with their new pet. I had seen cats before and knew they weren't supposed to be my friends, but I could take them or leave them."

"I never much cared for cats," Peaches interjected.

"I was waiting by the kitchen for one of the girls to come and get me, when the younger one came running down the hall, followed by her Siamese cat. I just waited. The girl ran right into the kitchen, but at the sight of me the cat careened to a stop, arched her back, glared, and began to give a mighty hiss. That hiss died aborning. That cat was so embarrassed to be frightened by a toy dog that she slunk back down the hall, secreted herself under a table, and wouldn't come out for hours."

Peaches chuckled, "You sure did get that cat, didn't you."

"You know, Peaches, I don't mind sitting up on top of this bookcase with you and that other stuffed animal that belonged to their daughters, but I surely do wish I could get down occasionally and have a spin around the house—or frighten a cat or two."

Honey Bear Arrives

Mary Dutton Smith

The week begins easily with a small "Learn to Ski Better" class at Bear Valley, plenty of snow, sunny days, learning to ski faster and faster. Friday morning I find our final exam means racing on the Nastar course, timed in seconds, two runs per skier.

My turn; crouching in position, leaning forward on poles, timer calling, "3 – 2 – 1 – go!" I push, jump, lean, turn, and follow the packed course almost blindly for at least ten seconds, classmates yelling, "Go – go!" behind me. I skid into the first turn following tracks, trying to go fast, but also to stay upright, barely missing the poles I must go around. Ahead of me is a large, white banner saying "FINISH" in black letters.

In an unthinking blur I charge into it and immediately fall backward, skis in the air, poles awry. This white banner is not made of paper—it is heavy, wet canvas. I am undone, completely entangled, feeling sore, lame, and stupid all at once. I have disconnected the timing mechanism, which means a delay for the other skiers. I should have gone *around* the banner.

A ski instructor helps me up, shaking his head in disbelief. I wobble toward the first aid station, feeling I should leave as soon as possible. After a checkup, one Band-Aid, and a sling for a possible sprain, I start toward the parking lot, feeling sorry for myself.

As I pass the ski shop, I catch sight of a large, light brown teddy bear in the window, wearing a parka, ski cap, mittens,

---

almost smiling. I think he needs a friend. No, *I* need a friend. Suddenly I need him. I want him. I buy him, parka and all. Ten minutes later, he is beside me on the front seat.

And that is how Honey Bear became part of our family. That was 23 years ago, and he is still on the sofa, almost smiling. 🐾

Honey Bear and the Coyotes

Mary Dutton Smith

Honey Bear liked taking care of the little bears Honey Do, Honey Don't, and Honey Bran, and most of the time he was very busy. But at night when the little bears were fast asleep, it was very quiet and Honey Bear felt just a little bit lonesome.

One night he heard some howling and helping and occasional barking outside the house. He looked out the window to see what was happening. There in the moonlit meadow were some animals, running and jumping, mostly in circles, big ones and little ones. They looked like a family. They were gray and brown. They were coyotes.

Honey Bear watched them, thinking, "I could do that with a little practice. It looks like fun!"

So the next night when the little bears finally fell asleep, Honey Bear slipped quietly off the sofa and out the back door to see the noisy coyote family. And that's just what they were, a few grownups and about five little ones, and one or two middle-sized ones. And they weren't going anywhere, just in circles, running and sometimes jumping over each other.

After a while Honey Bear started running too, and trying to jump with the coyotes. They didn't seem to mind. But Honey Bear wasn't used to running or jumping, or howling. Most bears don't howl; they don't know how. Honey Bear was getting out of breath. So he just sat down right in the middle of all the dancing coyotes. They finally stopped and sat next to him, looking a little sad.

One of the grownups said to him softly, "Honey Bear, you had better go back to bed. You weren't meant to be a coyote. You don't know how to dance in a circle and howl. But you're a very nice bear."

Honey Bear stood up slowly, since he was a little stiff and out of breath. "Thank you for letting me come," he said. "I think you are right. I need to be a bear."

So he went back to the sofa with his little bears, Honey Do, Honey Don't, and Honey Bran, and fell sound asleep until the next morning. He was still a bit stiff and a little bit sore, but very glad he was a bear.

In the Bag

Arlene Mueller

Madge rummaged through the pile of SALE purses at Penney's. She needed a purse for her son Brian's wedding. A purple one. A large one.

When she finally found a purse that looked right, she tried stuffing Stretch, the cloth giraffe, into it. The purse was too small.

She knew the young salesgirl was watching her. *Probably thinks I'm a senile senior out for the day.* True, she was 70, but certainly not senile. Today she felt young and full of mischief.

Digging deeper into the pile, she spotted a vivid purple one big enough for a bowler hat. The giraffe went in easily. *That's it!*

The salesgirl at the cash register stared at Madge before removing polka-dotted Stretch from the roomy purse.

As she reached for a bag, she asked, "Would you rather have me put your toy back in the purse?"

"Well...sure, it's for him. I mean... it's where he'll be...."

"I see...," the girl murmured.

Madge laughed when they got outside, "Stretch, no one would understand why I need you at Brian's wedding. They'd say I was acting strangely. That's why it's our secret."

In the car, Madge continued, "If we're going to pull this off, we've got some big hurdles ahead. First, we have to keep anyone from discovering the new purse. Then the toughest part will be getting to the church without you being snatched from me."

Earlier that morning her daughter, Caroline, had informed Madge that she would be sitting alone in the front pew at the wedding. Madge had protested, but Caroline insisted it was protocol.

Sitting by her bedroom window later that afternoon, watching the rain, loneliness wrapped around her shoulders, she had spotted Stretch, Brian's favorite childhood toy. She lifted the limp animal from her bookshelf and whispered into his torn ear: "Stretch, *you'll* keep me company in that front pew!"

Together they had headed for Penney's.

Madge was nearly caught that evening.

She was eating her supper in front of the bedroom TV when she heard, "Mom?" It was Caroline.

"Up here."

"I brought your invitation to the wedding shower," Caroline gushed, brushing raindrops from her coat. "I suppose we should get you a new dress...."

Then she spied the new purse lying on the bed. Holding it by the plastic handle, she asked, "What's *this*?"

"What do you *think* it is?"

"Where's the nice little clutch bag I bought to go with the dress and shoes? You're not thinking of...."

"I like the bright color," Madge interrupted. "I got it on sale today at Penney's." She turned her eyes to the TV, feeling a twinge of guilt.

Caroline left, looking suspiciously at the garish purse.

Madge took Stretch from the bookshelf and galloped him about the room. "Whew, that was close wasn't it?" She pulled his fabric eyelid over his single button eye—wink!

While shopping for kitchen gifts for the shower, Madge found pot holders with giraffe faces. One giraffe—she couldn't believe it—was winking!

"I love giraffes," Emily exclaimed at the party, giving Madge a hug. Had she just imagined that Brian smiled when he saw the pot holders?

"So far, so good," she told Stretch that evening.

"Stretch, remember how you and I and Brian used to talk in squeaky giraffe voices? How at lunchtime you'd stand on the kitchen table because your young, tightly stuffed legs wouldn't bend? How your embroidered smile reminded us that you weren't just a toy? And how your button eyes never blinked when I read stories? Oh, how Brian loved to pull an eyelid over your eye and squeal, 'Look, Mom, Stretch is winking!'

"When Brian went to kindergarten," she continued, stroking the chintz body, "you sat quietly on his bookshelf. How you loved it whenever Brian stayed home from school and he took you to bed with him.

"By middle school, I rescued you from Brian's clutter and placed you on my bedroom bookshelf.

"I was in the hospital recovering from my operation when Brian was in high school. How I laughed when he whipped you out from under his jacket and danced you on the bed."

She paused before whispering, "Remember how I held you when I was lonely after Hank's death?" She cuddled the faded toy under her chin. "But now," she announced to the room, "Brian is 36, an attorney, owns his condo and a sports car that I have trouble getting into—and will marry Emily next week."

She gently laid Stretch in the recliner, "God willing, you'll be with me at the wedding!"

On the morning of the wedding Madge had doubts about her escapade, but she took it as a good omen when her nephew, rather than Caroline, drove her to the church.

As she joined the family in the vestibule, her dress jacket hung over her arm, completely hiding the purse. Caroline adjusted Madge's necklace without seeing the purse and told her to put on her jacket.

Madge panicked.

Fortunately, Caroline turned to quiet her children so Madge used the distraction to step behind a coat rack, squeeze the purse between her knees, slip into the jacket, and reappear with the purse safely clutched at her back.

"Ready?" Caroline nudged her toward the usher.

"Ready," she stared into Caroline's eyes, as she offered one arm to the young man and swung the purse into full view with the other.

"M-O-T-H-E-R, what in the world...."

Madge giggled as she started down the aisle, *We've done it, Stretch!* Then she became the mother of the bridegroom—a sweet lady carrying a bulging, bright purple purse.

When Brian and Emily were at the altar, she eased Stretch from the purse onto her lap and kept her hand resting tenderly on him.

Madge was surprised at the end of the ceremony when the newlyweds paused at her pew. As Brian leaned to embrace her, he saw one-eyed Stretch staring at him. He paused a moment, then kissed his mother's forehead, tweaked Stretch's ear, and murmured, "Hi, there!"

He winked at both of them, put his arm around Emily's waist, and together they turned to their guests.

With a silent apology to Stretch, Madge stuffed him back into the purse.

Then she took the usher's arm and, with tears wetting her cheeks, walked into the afternoon sunshine.

After such excitement, Stretch would surely need a nap. 🐾

Imprints

Indian Lore

Lois Grisdale

Indian lore tells us
    An eagle exemplifies spirit,
    A cat, secrets, and
    A turtle stands for Mother Earth.
    A bear means introspection,
    A hummingbird, joy.
    A horse indicates power,
    A fox means camouflage.
    A lizard is for dreaming,
    A frog, cleansing.
    A dog for loyalty,
    A squirrel, gathering.
    A dragonfly is illusion.
    A wolf is a teacher. Then there's
Coyote, the jokester.

Horsefeathers!
or
What Happens When My Leisure Time and a Book of Word/Phrase Origins Come Together
Faye Morrison

Why on earth would anyone combine *horse* and *feathers?* Possibly to use a term in polite society that's more acceptable than *bull*....Or maybe it came from a remark that something was nonsensical, like saying "a horse has feathers." It's easy to spend hours trying to figure out American idioms, and interesting to find how many of them deal with animals. Maybe you think it's all *hogwash* (the *wash* refers to garbage fed to the hog; therefore, something essentially worthless) but it's *doggone* amazing to me.

Lots of our sayings are obvious in their origin and intent: strong as an ox, stubborn as a mule, blind as a bat, timid as a mouse. But where did *bull in a china shop* come from? The combination of bulky and delicate seems unwise, and the expression has been around since 1834 when it first appeared in a novel.

It's pretty easy to see that calling someone a *rat* would be derogatory, and a social *butterfly* would flit from place to place. A *fish out of water* would flop around frantically, but don't you wonder about *fish or cut bait?* This phrase has been associated with politics since the end of the 19th century and admonishes the candidate to take action or let someone else do it. Maybe it came from an impatient fisherman who needed the fishing spot of a procrastinator. Do you enjoy *flea markets?* We got that idea from a corruption of the Dutch word for *valley,* which became corrupted to *vlie* (pronounced *vlee.*) A New York market in Dutch Colonial days was located in the valley at the foot of Maiden Lane, and *vlie* gradually was replaced with the soundalike word, *flea*.

I've never understood why a *dog's life* would be so bad, although no one wants to be known as a *dirty dog*. A well-fed, adored pet has a pretty good existence in my book. But these expressions, along with *die like a dog* and *to go to the dogs,* come from cultures that don't value pets as we do. Where they aren't eaten, they are considered pests and scavengers; if fed at all, they get scraps to fight over. Well, have you ever seen it rain *cats and dogs?* The disgusting origin goes back to 17th century England when heavy rains produced city streets in full flood that included drowned cats and dogs.

Dog brings to my mind the regal Lassie—a noble picture— but no one would want to be referred to as a *dog in the manger,* churlishly guarding what you had whether you needed it or not. And a *dog eat dog* situation is to be avoided. The *dog tags* worn by servicemen got that nickname during World War I due to their resemblance to the metal license tag on a dog's collar. Having some of *the hair of the dog that bit you* goes way back to a Roman belief that "Like cures like"; they'd even have you wear bound hairs of the animal that chomped on you to hasten healing. From 1640, the expression was used to plead for a drink in the morning to cure the hangover from the night before.

Ever save your money in a *piggy bank?* Surprisingly, the first recorded use of the term was as recent as 1945. The connection between *pig* and *bank* is thought to relate to a pig's tendency to hoard food for himself. Does that have anything to do with *piggyback?* No. Actually the word should be *pickaback* and goes back over 300 years when it was first recorded as carrying a person, usually a child, on one's back. The change from *pickaback* to *piggyback* occurred over 100 years ago. And a *pigtail* didn't start out as the name of a hair arrangement. It was used hundreds of years ago to describe tobacco leaves twisted into a corkscrew.

And (ahem!) a couple of the less polite animal expressions. *Cat* was a term for a prostitute as long ago as 1401, so naturally *cathouse* came to mean brothel. And have you ever eaten *mountain oysters?* In France or Spain you'd see *bull's balls* on the menu, but in more inhibited American restaurants, the same item is listed as *mountain oysters* or *prairie oysters.*

Speaking of bulls, in the early 1900s baseball pitchers often warmed up under large Bull Durham Tobacco signs which offered 50 dollars to any batter whose home run hit the large brightly colored bull. That's one explanation for the origin of the *bull pen* where relief pitchers work out, or it could have come from the *bull pen* that was a stockade for prisoners in the early 1800s. A *bulldozer* which moves dirt actually got its name from political terrorists way before our time: Louisiana vigilantes prevented freed slaves from voting after the Civil War by whipping them, giving recipients a *dose of bull* or what the strength of a bull could do. *Bull dogs* don't resemble bulls, but they were bred for *bullbaiting,* a cruel and bloody sport outlawed in England in 1835.

Let's not go *hog wild* (from the farm, a reference to the way hogs become wildly excited when aroused). Enough of this *cock and bull story*—which probably came from a piece of fiction that entailed a cock and bull talking to each other. As neither animal can talk, the phrase came to mean any bit of blarney. We'll *pigeonhole* (compartments in old roll-top desks resembled the holes in dovecotes) the whole thing and go throw around the old *pigskin.* (Footballs were never made of pigskin, but were probably called that as in other early games animal bladders were kicked around.)

(The author acknowledges much help from *The Facts on File Encyclopedia of Word and Phrase Origins* by Robert Hendrickson.) 🐾

Loving Pets?

Barbara Conrad

I have loved my pets. Really, I have. And I have cared properly for each of them. I'm not sure they have extended the same loving concern to me.

Brownie, our sloe-eyed water spaniel, shared the back seat of our 1939 Chevrolet with me. She went everywhere we went. Many of our sojourns included visits to lakes and rivers where she would plunge in with abandon. One shake after her swim was never enough; she always had to have a second one after she got settled in the back seat next to me. Helping me learn the facts of life was Brownie's job. Her first litter included one more puppy than she had nipples to accommodate. What part of the lesson was that?

In my junior high school years I was allowed a cat of my own. Small, black, and very loyal, she would leap among the snowbanks to greet me when I came home from school. I named her for all my movie star favorites: Lana June Jeanne Esther. But she mostly came to "Kitty." One summer I had to take her with me on a long car trip with a friend because my parents were going away for the summer. And she was pregnant. I don't think the trip did her much good because when we finally got back home, she delivered a very deformed kitten. Oh, dear.

Newlyweds and acquisition of dogs go hand in hand. My new husband, John, and I were right there. Ours was a 70-pound boxer, Pete, who came to us with already-formed bad habits.

He failed dog school and would not stay home, but in contrast to his bad outdoor behavior, he allowed our baby to inspect his teeth and chew on his choker.

My gracious mother took him for a few months while we lived in an apartment, but he became canine non grata after grabbing a filet mignon off her barbeque. Gracious me.

For a few years we were content to have one Siamese cat, Abigail. She was more dog than most of the neighborhood dogs. She guarded our property from high atop the doorframe of our house and never allowed roving Rovers anywhere near our lawn. She was an incessant talker and had an uncanny knack of walking into a room of people and instantly spotting the person who hated cats or was wearing a black dress and immediately headed for one of those laps. For some reason we didn't have her spayed for quite a while and her multicolored litters showed her lack of discretion in mate choice. She was a good mother and when the kittens were all given away, she would carry my fuzzy black bedroom slippers around in anticipation of their needing her.

Our 10-year-old son, Douglas, was the recipient of a kitten that he got to watch being born. However, kitty George died too soon of leukemia. We asked Douglas if he wanted another kitty and he said yes. He and his sister brought home this tiny black thing that I didn't think was even six weeks old. But Roxie was feisty. Much feistier than kitty George and wanted to play and roughhouse, but Doug thought cats should snuggle and purr like George did in his short life.

One afternoon Doug was sitting with Roxie curled up in his hands when suddenly he flung her across the room. "She doesn't even love me!" he growled. It wasn't too long before they made up, and Roxie loved Doug until he was 27 years old.

We swore off dogs after Pete, the boxer, but several years later succumbed to a German shepherd mix when we acquired some country acreage and felt the need for a barker who would raise the warning about coyotes or other intruders. Our mistake. Hilda never barked. And she, too, would not stay home.

Eventually we moved to downtown where Hilda had a lovely dog run and dog house with a porch for sunning. She barked and barked and barked. She was in her glory when she ran away here. The Thrifty Drug Store across the street provided her with many licks of ice cream off the sidewalk from tops of cones children lost just outside the door. And the butcher never failed to slip her a bone from his back door. We always knew where to find her.

In our retirement years we have been travelers and not able to do right by a pet. I do miss the warmth of a cat curled up at my feet or a dog licking my hands in greeting. Fortunately our three children have nine cats and dogs among them so we never lack for something to pet. And I did see the cutest miniature Schnauzer puppy for sale last week....

Night Cries

Faye Morrison

An animal yelps desperately in the dead of the night, and I am instantly awakened. *What is that?* Even under the down comforter, I shiver, anticipating another anguished cry. It comes. Then again—sharp sounds tearing through the calm of darkness.

Chill replaces snugness as my comforter seems to lose heat. Looking out the window from the safety of bed, I weigh what must be happening. *Too frantic a cry for just a lonely domestic pet. This isn't the neighbor's dog left alone and lonely.* Logic tells me it must be a small animal—a fawn? cat? puppy?—caught by a nocturnal predator, perhaps a coyote, or a very small animal that could be picked up by an owl.

This is nature, Faye. Let it be. But the night seems darker, the sudden silence ominous. Danger hovers and the trees outside my window sway and moan in sympathy. Living alone isn't an adventure on a moonless night when an animal is in trouble.

Again, the yelping, farther away, weaker. Is the prey being carried off? Cornered and giving up? Was it perhaps a rabbit caught in his burrow?

The only nonviolent explanation I can come up with is the possibility of cats mating. But that would be a more continuous screeching accompanied by scuffling, not these intermittent yowls.

Quiet now. No rustling. No yelps. Whatever the drama, I think it's over, but my heart is beating faster than normal and my eyes are wide open. I re-settle under the covers, but can't bring back drowsiness, sedation. A warm body near mine would certainly help. A dark bedroom in the woods is a lonely place when I'm awakened by the sound of pain from the unknown. 🐾

Rescue in the Manzanita

Marian Cramer

Nosey, the cutest of the bunnies we owned, often sat in my lap on the patio during summer months while I read or wrote letters. Rabbits don't purr, but if Nosey could have purred, she would have. She was named for her distinguishing characteristic, a black nose, which was the only color on her otherwise white body.

Family ritual was to go to our cabin in Blue Lake Springs every few weekends and for most holidays and vacations. The kids wanted to take her when we went there. I loved that bunny and couldn't say no. Their dad looked at four pleading faces and set about constructing a box for Nosey.

The sturdy box had slats for air circulation and view. Nosey was a good traveler, and we set her up with food and water when we arrived at the cabin. We placed her box at the base of a tall pine tree close to the deck so she would always have shade and be cool. We all talked to her as we went back and forth unloading the car. She was happy, the kids were happy, I was happy, and Ken seemed glad she had come along with us.

We city slickers loved our small piece of mountain property and the rest and renewal it brought to our busy lives. We happily learned names of the trees and shrubs that surrounded us. It was fun being "mountain folk" but our ignorance of mountain dangers escaped us entirely.

Before we went to bed, Ken checked Nosey's box to be sure it was secure, told Nosey goodnight, and turned out the lights. Ah, the fresh air of the mountains and the quiet cabin did its usual magic. We slept.

About 2 a.m. something woke me up—something making a horrible noise and another something shrieking an equally horrible sound. I ran to the window, joined immediately by Ken, who said, "It's a fox." As he ran outside to chase it away, Nosey decided to rescue herself. Not realizing her safety inside the box, she managed to squeeze her body between the slats where it could not possibly fit. Panic is a powerful motivator. She was gone in a flash, now truly a hopping dinner dish for that fox.

Ken made a lot of noise hoping to scare the fox into the hills and then began to search for our terrified bunny. All the children were up by now and I had to put on my "stern mother" hat to keep them inside. They lined their chins on the window sill while I paced helplessly out onto the deck and back inside.

Ken's soft voice called, "Here, Nosey, come to Daddy." Even on this moonlit night he carried a flashlight to shine into the manzanita bushes, tentatively parting those thorny shrubs in desperate search. Such an odd picture, this grown man in his pajamas crawling around in the wee hours of the morning calling for a rabbit. I wondered if one day we would all laugh at this, or if the story would have a sad ending. I even asked myself, *Why is he calling her name like he thinks she'll come to him? She's a rabbit, for heaven's sake!* I didn't have a better suggestion so I kept quiet.

Suddenly I saw a flash of white bouncing toward the man on his knees in the bushes. Ken saw her, too, and slowly held out his hand and said, "Here, Nosey, come on." That bunny hopped right up to him and waited for him to pick her up.

Did she recognize his voice? Was it the soft kind tone she heard? How did she find her way back in this strange new environment? Her little heart was thumping as he handed her to me when we were all safe in the kitchen. While the kids welcomed Nosey with hugs and tears, a wiser dad moved the box into the downstairs bathroom where Nosey spent her mountain vacation nights ever after. 🐾

Whose Habitat?

Marlene Wiley Bradford

A mule deer buck made himself at home last year under our apple tree, on a small rise in our garden. He watched my husband, Dick, work outside and saw us come and go in our cars. Dick would speak softly to the buck. We called him Henry.

When I walked to my studio, I would quietly say, "Good morning, Henry. Are you feeling good today?" He would study me intently with his shiny large brown eyes and keep his ears still and alert. One warm day I opened the large garage door to my studio, not more than 15 feet from where Henry was lying, and thought he would bolt away. He remained still and peered into my studio as I worked.

We live among four kinds of oak trees at the top of a low hill, above a pond which is surrounded by 30 acres of undeveloped land. We had become good friends with our elderly next-door neighbor, as had his and our dogs, both corgis. Squirrels and birds drank from our dog's outdoor water bowl, but we didn't see many of our other native animals until about a year after our beloved dog died. Then, quail brought their chicks close to our house, and a wild turkey hen with four young ones put us on her itinerary.

When we first saw Henry, we were startled by his misshapen antlers. We wondered whether malnutrition was the cause, although a yearling buck in his herd also had similarly stunted antlers. Branches of Henry's were fused together and grew straight up, curving inward, his left antler standing twice as tall as the right one. I was able to count five tiny points jutting up from the top of his larger antler and three on the smaller one.

He held his head erect as though his rack was perfect. We felt honored to have the five-point monarch gracing our garden. In fact, we sacrificed part of it to him. He was much more interesting than our roses, petunias, and geraniums. I was concerned, however, about his diet. I had heard about a park ranger's report that mule deer have more than one stomach. Like cows, deer graze on various plants and then lie down to chew their cud. He had said when they eat the wrong kind of food, deer have been found dead of starvation with stomachs full of plants they've been unable to regurgitate and chew.

Fortunately for Henry our garden and the surrounding vegetation seemed to agree with him. His coat was becoming more lustrous and he was gaining weight. He also loved the grape leaves belonging to our neighbor, as well as his fruit trees and rose bushes. When Henry would wander next door, our neighbor's voice called out, "Go get 'em!" whereupon his corgi, Buffy, would bark and chase the deer back into our garden. Buffy knew where the property line was. While she never worried about crossing the line to come visit us, she did not cross it to chase the deer back to our place.

Henry didn't spend all of his time in our sanctuary. He often disappeared for several days. Sometimes he would sleep at night on the slope behind our shop where toyon and manzanita shielded him from the street below. A large doe gave birth to a fawn there. Near a home lower down our hill another doe gave birth to twins. After several weeks we saw the twins with "our" fawn behind our shop. We think they were a part of Henry's herd.

Henry had a small scar on his right hip and walked with a slight limp. One day I surprised both of us when he was standing near our back door as I opened it. He bolted down the hill toward the pond, halting abruptly at the barbed wire fence, and turned to look at me. I remembered other deer easily jumping over that fence and realized Henry's scar showed more than a superficial disability.

As their habitat is being changed, deer and other animals are of necessity learning to live in closer proximity to people. Homes are appearing on parcels of formerly undeveloped land everywhere in Calaveras County. We see vineyards with eight-foot fencing where deer formerly fed in open fields. At higher elevations acres of forests are being clear-cut. I worried about Henry when he was away during deer hunting season and was relieved each time he reappeared.

In January our neighbor died, and I brought Buffy to our house. Her eyes were dull with grief. She moved slowly and did not want us out of her sight. We petted her, fed her, and talked to her. When I first took her outside, Henry was lying under his tree. He stood up and stared at us. Buffy kept her eyes and nose to the ground and didn't see him. Henry walked away.

Several days later I saw six deer in our garden. When I took Buffy out, she picked up their scent and marked areas where they had been standing. She ran with her nose to the ground over to her yard, found the place where they had been lying in grass, and marked it also. She was on a rampage and I couldn't stop her. Later that day we saw nine deer standing near her vacant house. The deer slept beside the house for several more days. Then large dogs ran through that garden every morning, chasing them, and late in January all the deer left. I felt sad wondering whether Henry would ever return.

In March we saw a deer lying under our apple tree. Dick said, "Look who's here."

I thought it was a doe and then remembered Henry would have shed his antlers. I recognized the darker curly fur on his head and the small scar on his right hip. He walked away when Buffy came out. She picked up his scent and marked the little shallow place in the dirt where he had made his bed.

One day in June we saw Henry with another buck behind our shop. His new antlers were fused again, and larger than last year. Buffy seems to be following deer trails with her nose to the ground, but has not marked deer beds we see in our garden. We're glad to know Henry is around and spends his days out of harm's way. 🐾

Pets Beware!

Mary Dutton Smith

We always had a family pet, usually a dog. There was Cappie the collie, Frosty the spaniel, Heidi the beagle, Nick the Samoyed. All of us took care of them, but I never had total responsibility. I would forget to feed them. As you will see, I was just not dependable.

My first pets of my very own, when I was eight, were two beautiful goldfish in a clear glass bowl. For two weeks I fed them faithfully and changed the water on Saturday morning. The third week, I carefully tipped the bowl over the kitchen sink, and as I watched the water rush out, I saw two shining golden bodies slither under my fingers and disappear down the drain. I never saw them again.

Many months later, I was given a small brown turtle in a lovely terrarium. He needed very little care. One day I put him on the oriental rug to wander a little more freely. He did. It was hard to see him on the dark pattern of the rug. I went out to play. When I came back, he was gone.

Six months later, the vacuum cleaner found a small dried-up brown shell under the radiator.

When I became a research assistant at Columbia Medical School in New York City, I had cages of rats, mice, and rabbits to care for. Rats make wonderful pets, so I usually had one curled up in my lab coat pocket all day. Occasionally I took one home by mistake. That was no problem except for the time one peeked out on the New York subway, to the dismay of those standing next to me. I smiled and found an empty seat, and closed my pocket.

The female rats about to have litters were placed in separate cages on a quiet top shelf for their safety. Mitzi was a favorite. On a Monday morning, I reached up to her cage, and pulled back with a yelp of pain with Mitzi still chewing on my finger. She flew from my finger through the open seventh-floor window behind me. Mitzi disappeared. We never saw her again. Her just-born litter was given to new mothers.

As the title says, pets beware! 🐾

Animal Clichés

Barbara Conrad

People malign animals to fill intellectual vacuums when they cannot think of any expression but a cliché. I'm sure we've all said or written *sick as a dog, no spring chicken,* or *drink like a fish.* It's amazing to see the number of times we expect animals to rescue our inadequate speaking or writing.

Clichés pervade our language and we are all guilty of their use, even as we acknowledge that they have lost their flavor through overuse or are stale or meaningless. But in their defense, clichés provide a common denominator that we all understand. Someone said that the worst cliché is better than a bad phrase. Fifteen kinds of clichés have been identified in *Clichés: 1500 Phrases Explored and Explained.* Animals reside in every section.

Defining a cliché is not easy. Editors and word gurus seldom agree on definitions. Some we easily recognize when we see them, but many are archaic. They have become a kind of mental shorthand and through them animals have helped us have our say. The majority of animal clichés occur as idioms, but even in that classification, the definition is difficult. Its parts don't necessarily add up to a whole. The dictionary says idioms are a group of words established by usage where the meaning isn't clear from the individual words. What comes to mind is *you can take a horse to water, but you can't make him drink* or *let the cat out of the bag.* Neither of these makes sense in reality, but somehow we know what they really mean.

Similes, with their giveaway clues of *as* or *like,* and animal comparisons are a natural combination. *Quiet as a mouse* or *crazy like a fox* both meet the criterion.

We've all become used to hackneyed phrases from exposure to television ads and slang of the younger set. But even before ads, people bored each other with *eager beaver* or *wild horses would not drag it from me.* The latter comes from a medieval torture expression.

Non-biblical proverbs provide another source of clichés that relates to animals. An example dating back to the 1600s is *what is sauce for the goose is sauce for the gander.* This portended equality for women, but the proverb predated equality for several generations. Still in common use is *don't count your chickens before they hatch.*

Another animal-related cliché is one called a catchphrase, such as *see a man about a dog,* that we humorously associate with a person declining to tell his destination when he leaves the room—usually to go to the bathroom. It has not worn out its linguistic welcome after more than a hundred years of use. Another old one, *sure beats cock fighting,* is dying out, probably to be replaced by *sure beats a stick in the eye.*

Literary allusions include such gems as *pearls before swine,* which comes from a passage in the book of Matthew, "Neither cast ye pearls before swine." Another widely used biblical reference from Ecclesiastes is *the fly in the ointment,* which refers to an element that detracts from something otherwise pleasant.

Clichés come and wane and we continue to either use them or try not to. If experts like dictionary editors and lexicographers have difficulty defining a cliché, what are we to do? So I'll leave you with *the whole can of worms* that *you will know one when you see one* or *when it bites you on the leg.* 🐾

Raindrop pearls falling
refresh water lily pads
and cool croaking frogs.

Gwen Serrière

The Authors

Marlene Bradford. For the past 25 years I've been a clay sculptor of portrait busts and animals. I've always loved to write, and in my late 50s began taking classes in memoir writing. In 1992 I wrote a piece included in Kathy Crump's handmade paper book, *elegy for the UNCOMMON WOMAN,* now in the permanent collection of the Women's Art Museum of Washington, D.C. My stories appear in Murphys Writers' latest four books. As a desktop publisher I have published our group's last two books.

Barbara Conrad. Coming to my profession as a secondary educator in midlife provided previous opportunities to have read a great deal, which is supposed to be the prerequisite for writing well. I'm not sure I've read enough, but writing in all forms— email, snail mail, memoirs, or grocery lists—gives me pleasure. My professional writing, curriculum, helped hone my skills, but nothing has been so beneficial as the help and encouragement of the Murphys Writers. We rock, ladies.

Marian Cramer. I've been writing since I was old enough to hold a pencil. It began with gift thank you notes to my grandparents and never stopped. Being secretary of every organization in which I held membership was not a chore. Writing has been my lifetime psychiatrist as I find putting emotions in black and white brings perspective. I've had many articles printed in newspapers, a medical issue book printed by a self-help group founded in New York City, and I've participated in three of the Murphys Writers books. I write because I love doing it, but also because I have to.

Jo Raye Doyle. I spent most of my early years in school and church work in Chestnut Hill, Tennessee, in the foothills of the Smoky Mountains, and later received a master's degree in religious education from Northwestern University. Soon after moving to Murphys with my daughter, Sheila, I joined a writers' group here and published *My View*, a brief story of my family and other families. I have participated in joint publications by the group. I am 91. Writing remains of great importance to me.

Carolyn Greenwood. Leaving a career of interior design behind me, I now call myself the Grandma Moses of literature, identifying myself solely on the basis of starting my interest in writing after my thirteenth grandchild was born. I had a grandiose plan for a novel, a fabulous love story set in Italy during the Gulf War. I fantasized that it would become a best seller with a movie to follow. I went so far as to construct in my mind the receiving of a literary award from a major university for having produced, at such an old age, a first novel that became a best seller. Reality set in when I signed up for the Murphys Writers class and realized how little I knew. I've been practicing for my novel ever since.

Marjorie Griffith. "Mommy, I love you so much it hurts me inside!" This from my four-year-old son as he grabbed me about my leg with a tight hug. Tears came to my eyes as I resolved to write a poem to preserve this beautiful moment. It soon became a habit to jot out poems, then short stories. When the time came to write our family history, I had many small anecdotes to help my memory. Writing stories about life events has been ongoing ever since.

Lois Grisdale. Drawing, painting, and printmaking have been my passion. My art has been exhibited in Europe and the U.S. I found the Murphys Writers in 1997, hoping it would help me catalog and describe my work, and found writing to be a great healing art.

Jane Lang. Possessing a vivid imagination and dramatic flair, I majored in speech and drama at Grinnell College and pursued a career as a speech therapist in the public schools, concentrating on verbal skills. About 12 years ago when I was 72, Arlene Mueller's memoir classes inspired me to focus my attention on the written word. My only previous creative writing experience consisted of composing campfire skits for summer programs. In 2003, the *Grinnell Alumni Magazine* published my story about college days, and several of my stories have appeared in four books published by the Murphys Writers.

Faye Morrison. I published my first piece in the *Oakland Tribune* when I was nine years old—in the Sunday children's supplement. I progressed to high school journalism and college English papers, followed by years when I never sat still long enough to write. Late in my teaching career I wrote curriculum and educational articles, even coauthored a book for teachers and librarians. Now I savor connection with the Murphys Writers, who truly care about the turn of a phrase.

Arlene Mueller. I founded Murphys Writers in 1993 and led it for 10 years. I am proud of the group as they add a fifth book to their collection. My love affair with writing began when I was still in my crib, preferring a pencil to a rattle. I went on to teach writing and publish short stories, poetry, newsletters, advertising copy, a newspaper column, travel articles, even a couple of cookbooks, and of course Letters to the Editor about everyone else's shortcomings. Writing has always been a way of trying to make sense of life. I wish I could write the world into better shape.

Grace Muirhead. Until recently writing was a drudge for me. After spending years correcting other people's efforts as an English teacher and a technical editor, I found that the very traits that brought success to an editor were enemies to putting original words on paper. After I finally decided to write first, criticize later, I surprised myself by actually enjoying the act of filling a blank page with thought, stories, and poems even though they were far from perfect. Were it not for the Murphys Writers, I might have continued to deny myself one of the great pleasures I find in retirement. My husband and I now write theater reviews for *The Union Democrat*. (My sentences are still too long, though.)

Jan Overstreet. Louisa May Alcott led me to want to write. I could just see Jo March curled up in the attic, "scribbling" away, and I was madly jealous. So I decided I could do that, too. I love writing, though the quality of my own writing sometimes falls far short of what I had hoped to accomplish. I suspect the moral there is "keep writing," and hope it will get better as I struggle along. For me, poetry is far easier than prose (depending on the day!).

Yolanda Randlett. My first major publication was in high school in a national anthology of poetry. I'll admit that was over forty years ago. Maybe it was also the last time I was published because my life took a major shift into the gaping mouth of American medicine. At first I was the patient, with matters of the heart. My survival inspired me to become a provider, with matters of the teeth. Next I ventured into money matters, facing the gigantic challenges of finance and administration that our health care system delivers. Now that I am free of it all, I'm returning to my first love—the printed word.

Gwen Serrière. It seems I've been writing stories since I was first able to hold a pencil. At about junior high stage I discovered the wonders of poetry as well, and have been dashing off little bits and bobs on oddball scraps of paper, in journals, and anywhere else I can find ever since. The Murphys Writers group has been a really great resource the last few years—a terrific sounding board and a fine circle of women. In recent years I've dabbled in local journalism, a wonderful discipline for honing concise writing skills, but I am now back to personal memoirs and poetry, my first love.

Nancy Shacklett. I have been writing all my life, mainly in letter and diaries. When I retired, I published two family genealogies, two family memoirs, and three books for my grandchildren. In 1990 I was inspired to take a class in memoir writing and had a wonderful time reflecting on and writing about my own life. It has been both joy and therapy.

Mary Dutton Smith. I don't think I ever had a choice. Mother was an English, Latin, and Greek scholar, and *everyone* learned to write—thank you letters, birthday cards, diaries, and "notes." My first note was probably "I promise not to hit my sister again," or "I will make my bed every morning." We all kept journals or diaries, or wrote long letters home when we had adventures. Most of mine were true, but not all.

Illustrated by
Lois Grisdale